It's another Quality Book from CGP

This book is for anyone doing GCSE Double Science at Higher Level.

Whatever subject you're doing it's the same
old story — there are lots of facts and you've just got
to learn them. GCSE Double Science Biology is no different.

Happily this CGP book gives you all that important
information as clearly and concisely as possible.

It's also got some daft bits in to try and make the whole
experience at least vaguely entertaining for you.

What CGP is all about

Our sole aim here at CGP is to produce the highest quality
books — carefully written, immaculately presented and
dangerously close to being funny.

Then we work our socks off to get them out to you
— at the cheapest possible prices.

Contents

Page References for Modular Syllabuses

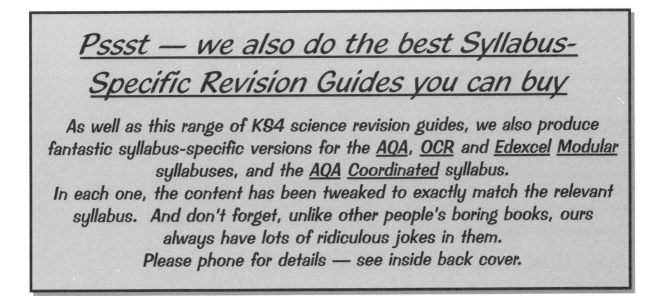

Published by Coordination Group Publications Ltd.
Typesetting and Layout by The Science Coordination Group
Illustrations by: Sandy Gardner, e-mail: illustrations@sandygardner.co.uk
                    and Bowser, Colorado USA.

Updated by:
Chris Dennett
James Paul Wallis
Dominic Hall
Suzanne Worthington

ISBN   1 841146 602 6

With thanks to David Worthington, Eileen Worthington and Taissa Csáky for the proofreading.

Groovy website: www.cgpbooks.co.uk

Printed by Elanders Hindson, Newcastle upon Tyne.
Clipart sources: CorelDRAW and VECTOR.

Cells, Tissues and Organ Systems

Plant Cells and Animal Cells Have Their Differences

You need to be able to draw these two cells with all the details for each.

Animal Cell

Plant Cell

4 THINGS THEY BOTH HAVE IN COMMON:

3 EXTRAS THAT ONLY THE PLANT CELL HAS:

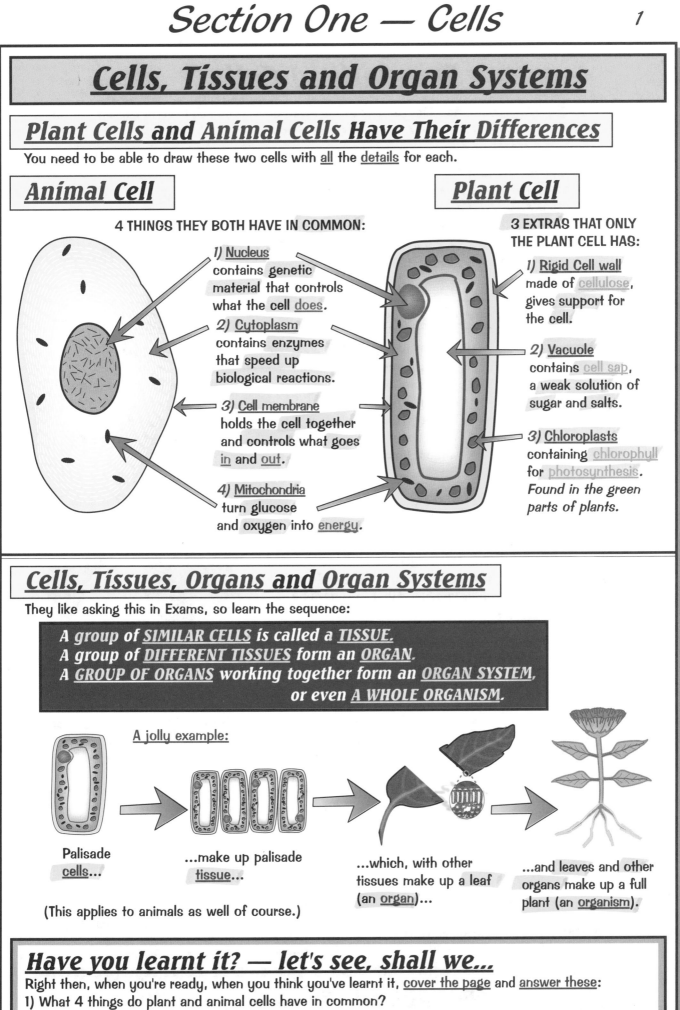

1) Nucleus contains genetic material that controls what the cell does.

2) Cytoplasm contains enzymes that speed up biological reactions.

3) Cell membrane holds the cell together and controls what goes in and out.

4) Mitochondria turn glucose and oxygen into energy.

1) Rigid Cell wall made of cellulose, gives support for the cell.

2) Vacuole contains cell sap, a weak solution of sugar and salts.

3) Chloroplasts containing chlorophyll for photosynthesis. Found in the green parts of plants.

Cells, Tissues, Organs and Organ Systems

They like asking this in Exams, so learn the sequence:

A group of **SIMILAR CELLS** is called a **TISSUE**.
A group of **DIFFERENT TISSUES** form an **ORGAN**.
A **GROUP OF ORGANS** working together form an **ORGAN SYSTEM**, or even **A WHOLE ORGANISM**.

A jolly example:

Palisade cells...

...make up palisade tissue...

...which, with other tissues make up a leaf (an organ)...

...and leaves and other organs make up a full plant (an organism).

(This applies to animals as well of course.)

Have you learnt it? — let's see, shall we...

Right then, when you're ready, when you think you've learnt it, cover the page and answer these:
1) What 4 things do plant and animal cells have in common?
2) What are the 3 differences between them?
3) Draw a sequence from cells to organism for a plant.

Specialised Cells

Most cells are specialised for a specific job, and in the Exam you'll probably have to explain why the cell they've shown you is so good at its job. It's a lot easier if you've already learnt them!

1) Palisade Leaf Cells are Designed for Photosynthesis

1) Packed with chloroplasts for photosynthesis.
2) Tall shape means a lot of surface area exposed down the side for absorbing CO_2 from the air in the leaf.
3) Tall shape also means a good chance of light hitting a chloroplast before it reaches the bottom of the cell.

2) Guard Cells are Designed to Open and Close

1) Special kidney shape which opens and closes the stomata (a single pore is a stoma) as the cells go turgid or flaccid.
2) Thin outer walls and thickened inner walls make this opening and closing function work properly.
3) They open to allow gases in and out for photosynthesis.
4) They're also sensitive to light and close at night to conserve water without losing out on photosynthesis.

3) Red blood cells are Designed to Carry Oxygen

1) Doughnut shaped to allow maximum oxygen absorption by the haemoglobin they contain. The function is similar to the palisade cells above. They are doughnut shaped rather than tall to allow smooth passage through the capillaries.
2) They are so packed with haemoglobin that they have no room for a nucleus.

4) Sperm and egg cells are specialised for Reproduction

Egg

Size of sperm in relation to the egg

Sperm

1) The egg cell has huge food reserves to provide nutrition for the developing embryo.
2) When a sperm fuses with the egg, the egg's membrane instantly changes to prevent any more sperm getting in.
3) A long tail gives the sperm the mobility needed for its long journey to find the egg.
4) The sperm also has a short life-span so only the fittest survive the race to the egg.

If you're doing the **OCR A** syllabus you have to learn that living things show these 7 life processes:

Use this little jollyism "MRS NERG" to remind you of the first letter of each word.

M — Movement ...... being able to **move** parts of the body
R — Reproduction .. producing **offspring**
S — Sensitivity ...... **responding** to the outside world
N — Nutrition .... getting **food** in where it's needed
E — Excretion .... **getting rid** of waste products
R — Respiration ..... turning **food into energy**
G — Growth .... getting to **adult size**

Blood Lolly — Special-iced Cells...

When you think you've learnt everything on this page, cover it up. Now sketch the four specialised cells mentioned on this page and point out their special features.

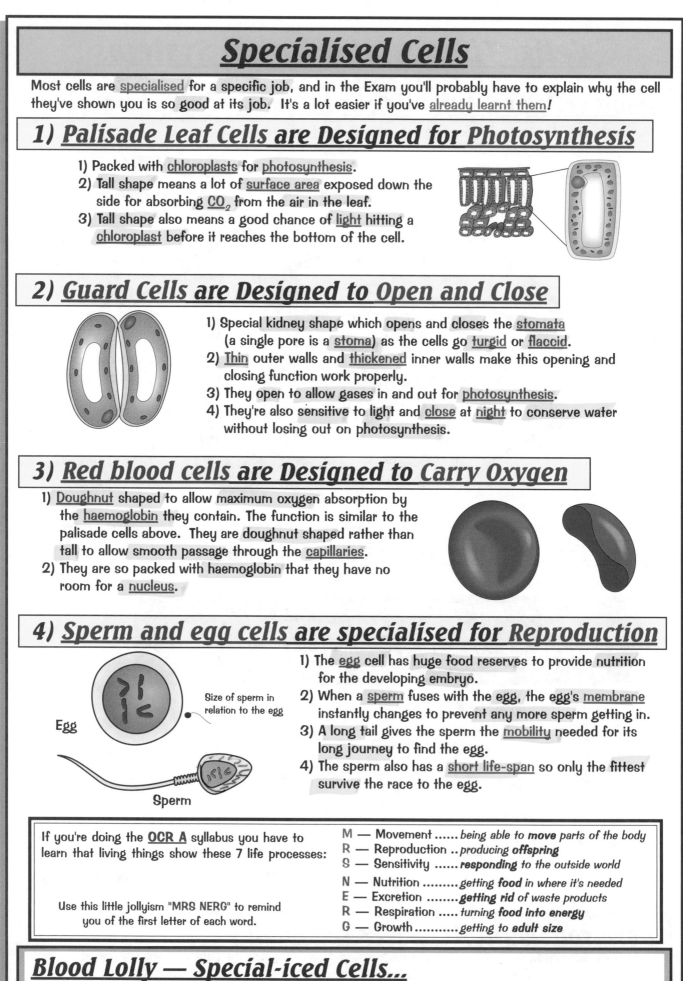

Diffusion

Don't be put off by the fancy word

"Diffusion" is really simple. It's just the <u>gradual movement</u> of particles from places where there are <u>lots</u> of them to places where there are less of them.

That's all it is — <u>it's just the natural tendency for stuff to spread out</u>.

Unfortunately you also have to <u>learn</u> the fancy way of saying the same thing, which is this:

> ### DIFFUSION is the PASSIVE MOVEMENT OF PARTICLES from an area of HIGH CONCENTRATION to an area of LOW CONCENTRATION

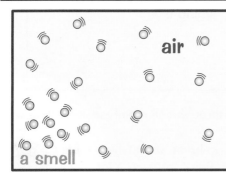

air

a smell

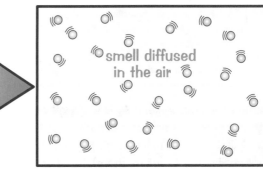

smell diffused in the air

Diffusion of Gases in Leaves is vital for Photosynthesis

The <u>simplest type</u> of diffusion is where different gases diffuse through each other, like when a weird smell spreads out through the air in a room. Diffusion of gases also happens in <u>leaves</u> and they'll very likely put it in your Exam. So learn it now:

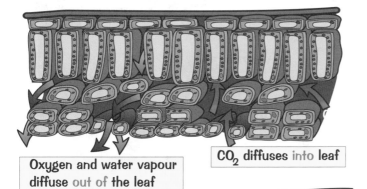

Oxygen and water vapour diffuse out of the leaf

CO_2 diffuses into leaf

Hot dry wind
good for carrying the water vapour away

For photosynthesis to happen, <u>carbon dioxide</u> gas has to get <u>inside</u> the leaves.
It does this by diffusion through the biddy little holes under the leaf called <u>stomata</u>.

At the same time <u>water vapour</u> and <u>oxygen</u> diffuse <u>out</u> through the same biddy little holes.

The water vapour escapes by diffusion because there's a lot of it <u>inside</u> the leaf and less of it in the <u>air outside</u>. This diffusion causes <u>transpiration</u> and it goes <u>quicker</u> when the air around the leaf is kept <u>dry</u> — i.e. transpiration is quickest in <u>hot</u>, <u>dry</u>, <u>windy conditions</u> — and don't you forget it!

Diffusion — Silent but deadly...

Yeah sure it's a pretty book but actually the big idea is to <u>learn</u> all the stuff that's in it.
So learn this page until you can answer these questions <u>without having to look back</u>:

1) Write down the fancy definition for diffusion, and then say what it means in your own words.
2) Draw the cross-section of the leaf with arrows to show which way the three gases diffuse.
3) What weather conditions make the diffusion of water vapour out of the leaf go fastest?

Diffusion Through Cell Membranes

Cell membranes are kind of clever...

They're kind of clever because they hold everything <u>inside</u> the cell, but, they let stuff <u>in and out</u> as well.
Only very <u>small molecules</u> can diffuse through cell membranes though — things like <u>glucose</u> or <u>amino acids</u>.

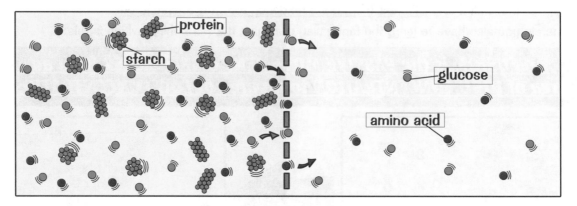

1) Notice that <u>big molecules</u> like <u>starch</u> or <u>proteins</u> can't diffuse through cell membranes — they could quite cheerfully ask you exactly that in the Exam.

2) Just like with diffusion in air, particles flow through the cell membrane from where there's a <u>high concentration</u> (a lot of them) to where there's a <u>low concentration</u> (not such a lot of them).

Gas Exchange in the Lungs

The <u>lungs</u> contain millions and millions of little air sacs called <u>ALVEOLI</u> (see diagram opposite) which are specialised to maximise the <u>diffusion</u> of oxygen and CO_2. The <u>alveoli</u> are an ideal <u>exchange surface</u>. They have:

1) An <u>enormous</u> surface area (about 70m² in total).
2) A <u>moist lining</u> for dissolving gases.
3) Very <u>thin walls</u>.
4) A <u>copious</u> blood supply.

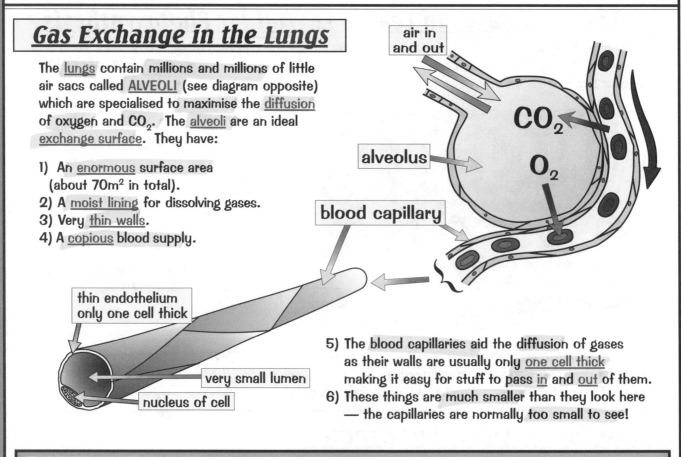

5) The blood capillaries aid the diffusion of gases as their walls are usually only <u>one cell thick</u> making it easy for stuff to pass <u>in</u> and <u>out</u> of them.

6) These things are much smaller than they look here — the capillaries are normally too small to see!

Al Veoli — The Italian Gas Man...

The big idea is that you should <u>understand and remember</u> what goes on and why it all works so well.
A clear visual image in your head of these diagrams makes it a lot easier.
<u>Learn</u> the diagrams, words and all, until you can sketch them out <u>entirely from memory</u>.

Active Uptake

Sometimes substances need to be absorbed against the concentration gradient i.e. from a lower to a higher concentration. This process is lovingly referred to as ACTIVE UPTAKE.

Root Hairs take in Minerals using Active Uptake

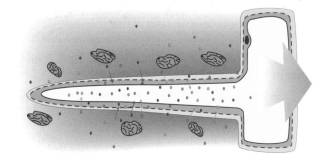

Root Hair cell

1) The cells on plant roots grow into long "hairs" which stick out into the soil.

2) This gives the plant a big surface area for absorbing water and minerals from the soil.

3) The concentration of minerals is higher in the root hair cell than in the soil around it.

4) So normal diffusion doesn't explain how minerals are taken up into the root hair cell.

5) They should go the other way if they followed the rules of diffusion.

6) The answer is that a conveniently mysterious process called "active uptake" is responsible.

7) Active uptake allows the plant to absorb minerals against the concentration gradient.
   This is essential for its growth. But active uptake needs energy from respiration to make it work.

8) Active uptake also happens in humans, in taking glucose from the gut (see below), and from the kidney tubules.

We need Active Uptake to stop us Starving

Active uptake is used in the gut when there is a low concentration of nutrients in the gut, but a high concentration of nutrients in the blood.

1) When there's loads of glucose, amino acids, fatty acids and glycerol in the gut they diffuse naturally into the blood.

2) BUT — sometimes there are fewer nutrients in the gut than there are in the blood.

3) This means that the concentration gradient is the wrong way.

4) The same process used in plant roots is used here....
   ..."Active uptake".

Inside the gut

The small molecules diffuse into the blood...

5) Active uptake allows nutrients to be taken into the gut, despite the fact that the concentration gradient is the wrong way.

Active Uptake sucks...

Make sure you can do these with the page covered up — if you can't, you ain't learnt nothin':

1) What type of molecules will diffuse through cell membranes and what type won't?
2) Give two examples of each.
3) Draw a full diagram of a root hair and say what it does.

Osmosis

Osmosis is a Special Case of Diffusion, that's all

> Osmosis is the movement of water molecules across a partially permeable membrane from a region of high water concentration to a region of low water concentration.

1) A partially permeable membrane is just one with real small holes in it. So small, in fact, that only water molecules can pass through them, and bigger molecules like glucose can't.

2) Visking tubing is a partially permeable membrane that you should learn the name of. It's also called dialysis tubing because it's used in kidney dialysis machines.

3) The water molecules actually pass both ways through the membrane in a two-way traffic.

4) But because there are more on one side than the other there's a steady net flow into the region with fewer water molecules, i.e. into the stronger solution (of glucose).

5) This causes the glucose-rich region to fill up with water. The water acts like it's trying to dilute it, so as to "even up" the concentration either side of the membrane.

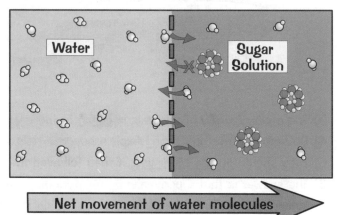

Net movement of water molecules

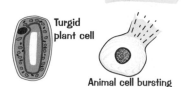

Turgid plant cell

Animal cell bursting

6) OSMOSIS makes plant cells swell up if they're surrounded by weak solution and they become TURGID. This is real useful for giving support to green plant tissue and for opening stomatal guard cells.

7) Animal cells don't have a cell wall and can easily burst if put into pure water because they take in so much water by osmosis.

Two Osmosis Experiments — Favourites for the Exams

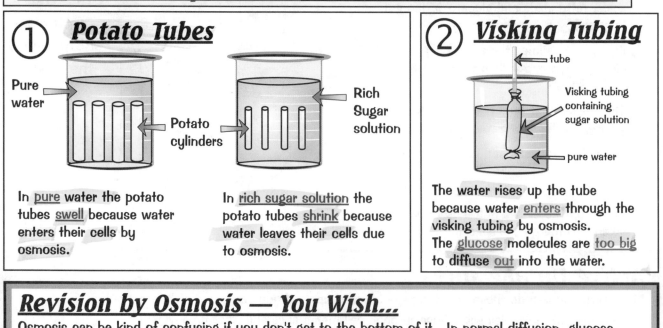

① Potato Tubes

Pure water

Potato cylinders

Rich Sugar solution

In pure water the potato tubes swell because water enters their cells by osmosis.

In rich sugar solution the potato tubes shrink because water leaves their cells due to osmosis.

② Visking Tubing

tube

Visking tubing containing sugar solution

pure water

The water rises up the tube because water enters through the visking tubing by osmosis. The glucose molecules are too big to diffuse out into the water.

Revision by Osmosis — You Wish...

Osmosis can be kind of confusing if you don't get to the bottom of it. In normal diffusion, glucose molecules move, but with small enough holes they can't. That's when only water moves through the membrane, and then it's called osmosis. Easy peasy, I'd say. Learn and enjoy.

Revision Summary for Section One

This is a short and easy section, that's for sure. But easy stuff means easy marks, and you'd better make sure you get all the easy marks — every last one. There's nothing quite as spectacularly dumb as working really hard at the difficult stuff and then forgetting about the easy bits. Here're some tough questions for you. Practise them over and over and over until you can just glide through them all, like a swan or something.

1) Copy the diagrams below and complete the labels adding a brief description for each one.

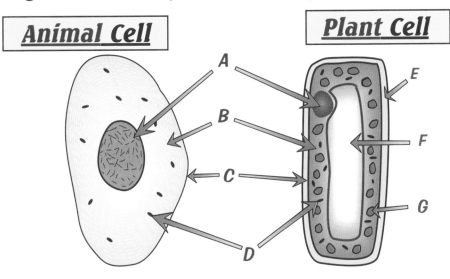

Animal Cell

Plant Cell

2) Sketch two specific plant cells.

3) Explain how each of the cells is specialised.

4) Sketch two different animal cells.

5) Explain how each of the cells is specialised.

6) <u>OCR A</u> syllabus only: Name and describe the seven life processes.

7) Fill in the blanks in this sequence: cells.. → ..tissue.→ organ → organism:

8) Give an example of this sequence in plants.

9) Give the strict definition of diffusion.

10) Sketch how a smell diffuses through air in a room.

11) Why are cell membranes kinda clever?

12) What will and won't diffuse through cell membranes?

13) Where in the body are the alveoli?

14) Name 4 specialisations that make the alveoli an ideal exchange surface?

15) a) What happens at root hairs?   b) What process is involved?

   c) Which process *won't* work there?

16) Give the full strict definition of osmosis.

17) What does osmosis do to plant and animal cells in pure water?

18) What is Visking tubing? What will and won't pass through it?

19) Give full details of the potato tubes experiment and the Visking tubing experiment.

Basic Plant Structure

You have to know all these parts of the plant and what they do:

The Five Different Bits of a Plant all do Different Jobs

1) Flower

This attracts insects such as bees which carry pollen between different plants. This allows the plants to pollinate and reproduce.

This is so exciting there's more about it on the next page.

2) Leaf

It produces food for the plant. I'll say it again, listen.... The leaf produces all the food that the plant needs.

Plants do not take food from the soil. Plants make all their own food in their leaves using photosynthesis.

(That's a bit of a shocker when you think about it. Imagine making all your own food under your skin just by lying in the sun — and never having to eat at all!)

3) Stem

1) This holds the plant upright.
2) Also, water and food travel up and down the stem.

5) Root

1) Its main job is anchorage.
2) It also takes in water and a few mineral ions from the soil. But mostly just water. Remember, plants do not take "food" in from the soil.

4) Root hairs

These give a big surface area to absorb water and ions from the soil.

The Big Idea is to LEARN All That...

Everything on this page is there to be learnt because it's very likely to come up in your Exams. This is pretty basic stuff, but it can still catch you out if you don't learn it properly. For example: "What is the main function of the root?". Too many people answer that with "Taking food in from the soil" — Eeek! LEARN these facts. They all count. They're all worth marks in the Exam. Practise until you can sketch the diagram and scribble down all the details, without looking back.

Leaf Structure

Leaves are Designed for One Thing Only...
— Making Food by Photosynthesis

The whole structure of leaves is geared towards that. Make sure you learn this diagram with all its labels:

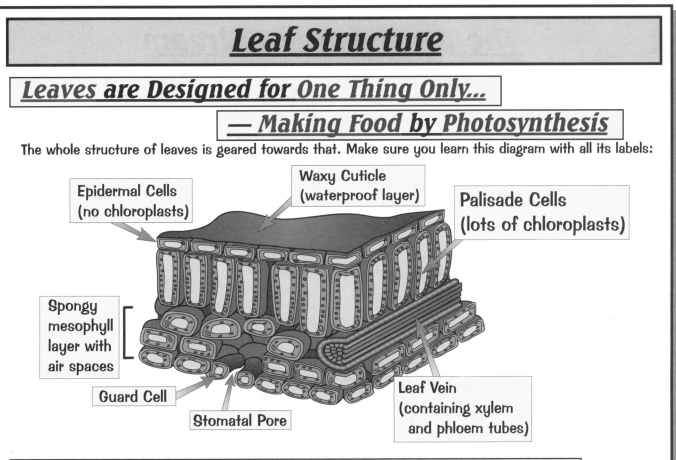

Epidermal Cells (no chloroplasts)

Waxy Cuticle (waterproof layer)

Palisade Cells (lots of chloroplasts)

Spongy mesophyll layer with air spaces

Guard Cell

Stomatal Pore

Leaf Vein (containing xylem and phloem tubes)

Learn all these Important Features about Leaves

1) The cells in the palisade layer are packed with chloroplasts which contain lots of chlorophyll. This is where the photosynthesis goes on.

2) The palisade and spongy layers are full of air spaces to allow CO_2 to reach the palisade cells.

3) The cells in the epidermis make wax which covers the leaf surface, especially the top surface. This is to limit water loss.

4) The lower surface is full of biddy little holes called stomata. They are there to let CO_2 in. They also allow water to escape — this is how the transpiration stream comes about.

5) Xylem and phloem vessels cover the whole leaf like tiny 'veins', to deliver water to every part of the leaf and then to take away the food produced by the leaf.

Stomata are Pores which Open and Close Automatically

1) Stomata close automatically when supplies of water from the roots start to dry up.

2) The guard cells control this. When water is scarce, they become flaccid, and they change shape, which closes the stomatal pores.

3) This prevents any more water being lost, but also stops CO_2 getting in, so the photosynthesis stops as well.

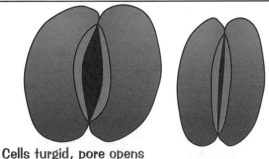

Cells turgid, pore opens

Cells flaccid, pore closes

Spend some time poring over these facts...

Two spiffing diagrams and a few simple features. What could be easier? Check the clock and give yourself five minutes of intense active learning to see how much you can learn.
"Intense active learning" means covering the page and scribbling down the details, but don't take 5 minutes drawing out a neat diagram of a leaf — that's just a waste of precious time.

The Transpiration Stream

Transpiration is the loss of water from the Plant

1) It's caused by the <u>evaporation</u> of water from inside the leaves.
2) This creates a slight shortage of water in the leaf which draws more water up from the rest of the plant which in turn draws more up from the <u>roots</u>.
3) It has <u>two</u> beneficial effects: a) it transports <u>minerals</u> from the soil;   b) it <u>cools</u> the plant.

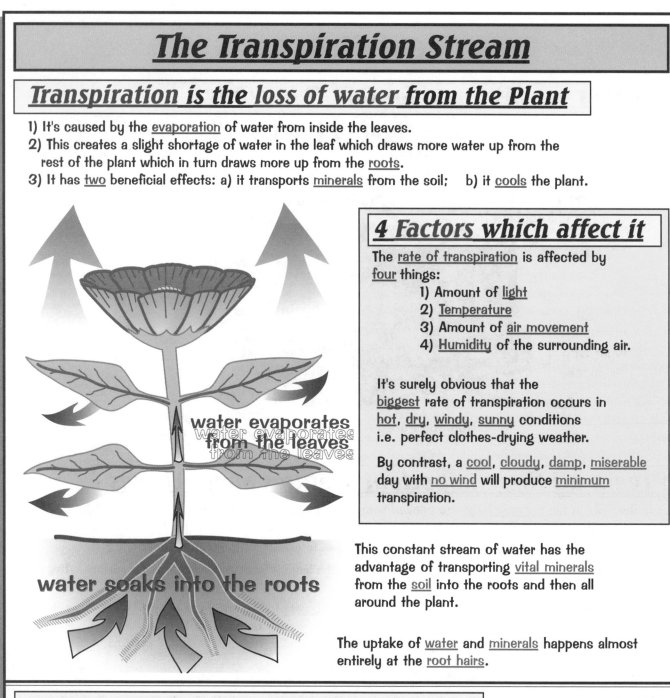

water evaporates
from the leaves

water soaks into the roots

4 Factors which affect it

The <u>rate of transpiration</u> is affected by <u>four</u> things:
  1) Amount of <u>light</u>
  2) <u>Temperature</u>
  3) Amount of <u>air movement</u>
  4) <u>Humidity</u> of the surrounding air.

It's surely obvious that the <u>biggest</u> rate of transpiration occurs in <u>hot</u>, <u>dry</u>, <u>windy</u>, <u>sunny</u> conditions i.e. perfect clothes-drying weather.

By contrast, a <u>cool</u>, <u>cloudy</u>, <u>damp</u>, <u>miserable</u> day with <u>no wind</u> will produce <u>minimum</u> transpiration.

This constant stream of water has the advantage of transporting <u>vital minerals</u> from the <u>soil</u> into the roots and then all around the plant.

The uptake of <u>water</u> and <u>minerals</u> happens almost entirely at the <u>root hairs</u>.

Turgor Pressure Supports Plant Tissues

1) When a plant is well watered, all its cells will draw water into themselves by <u>osmosis</u> and become <u>turgid</u>.
2) The contents of the cell start to push against the cell wall, kind of like a balloon in a shoebox, and thereby give <u>support</u> to the plant tissues.
3) <u>Leaves</u> are entirely supported by this turgor pressure. We know this because if there's no water in the soil, a plant starts to <u>wilt</u> and the leaves <u>droop</u>. This is because the cells start to lose water and thus <u>lose</u> their turgor pressure.

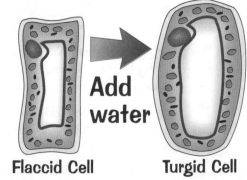

Add water

Flaccid Cell   Turgid Cell

It helps if you're quick on the uptake...

There's quite a lot of information on this page. You could try learning the numbered points, but you'll find a better plan is to do a "<u>mini-essay</u>" on transpiration and write down everything you can think of. Then look back to see what you've forgotten. Then do it again! <u>Till you get it all</u>.

Transport Systems in Plants

Plants need to transport various things around inside themselves. They have tubes for it.

Phloem and Xylem Vessels Transport Different Things

1) Plants have two separate sets of tubes for transporting stuff around the plant.
2) Both sets of tubes go to every part of the plant, but they are totally separate.
3) They usually run alongside each other.

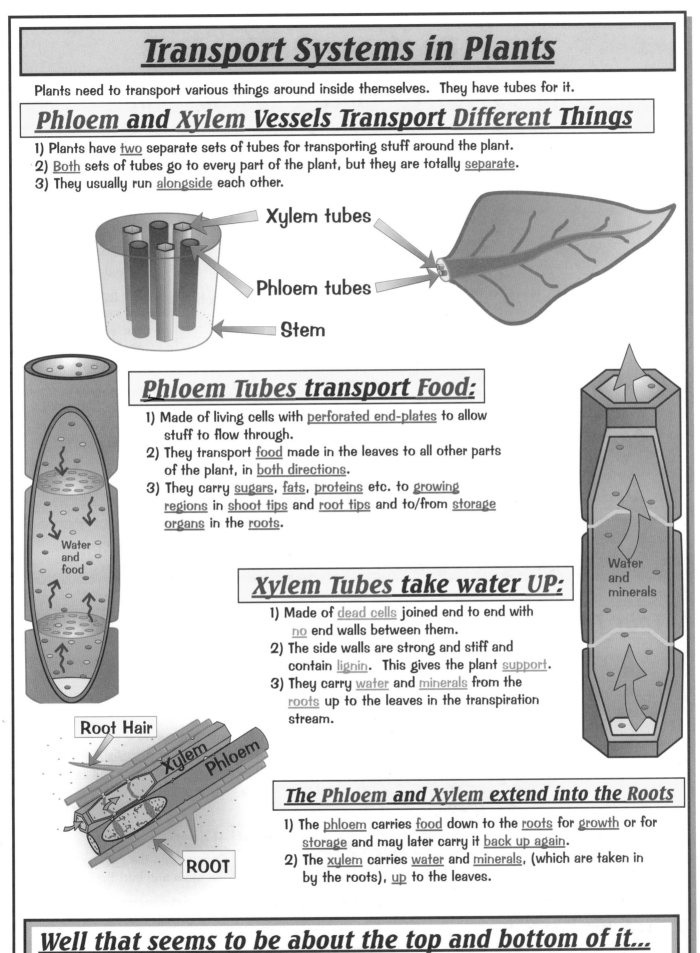

Xylem tubes

Phloem tubes

Stem

Phloem Tubes transport Food:

1) Made of living cells with perforated end-plates to allow stuff to flow through.
2) They transport food made in the leaves to all other parts of the plant, in both directions.
3) They carry sugars, fats, proteins etc. to growing regions in shoot tips and root tips and to/from storage organs in the roots.

Water and food

Xylem Tubes take water UP:

1) Made of dead cells joined end to end with no end walls between them.
2) The side walls are strong and stiff and contain lignin. This gives the plant support.
3) They carry water and minerals from the roots up to the leaves in the transpiration stream.

Water and minerals

Root Hair

Xylem

Phloem

ROOT

The Phloem and Xylem extend into the Roots

1) The phloem carries food down to the roots for growth or for storage and may later carry it back up again.
2) The xylem carries water and minerals, (which are taken in by the roots), up to the leaves.

Well that seems to be about the top and bottom of it...

This is an easy page. There are important differences between xylem and phloem tubes. Make sure you know all the numbered points on this page, and the diagrams. Then cover the page and scribble it all down with detailed sketches of the diagrams. Then do it again, until you get it all.

Section Two — Plants

Photosynthesis

Photosynthesis Produces Glucose from Sunlight

1) <u>Photosynthesis</u> is the process that produces 'food' in plants. The 'food' it produces is <u>glucose</u>.

2) Photosynthesis takes place in the <u>leaves</u> of all <u>green plants</u> — this is what leaves <u>are for</u>.

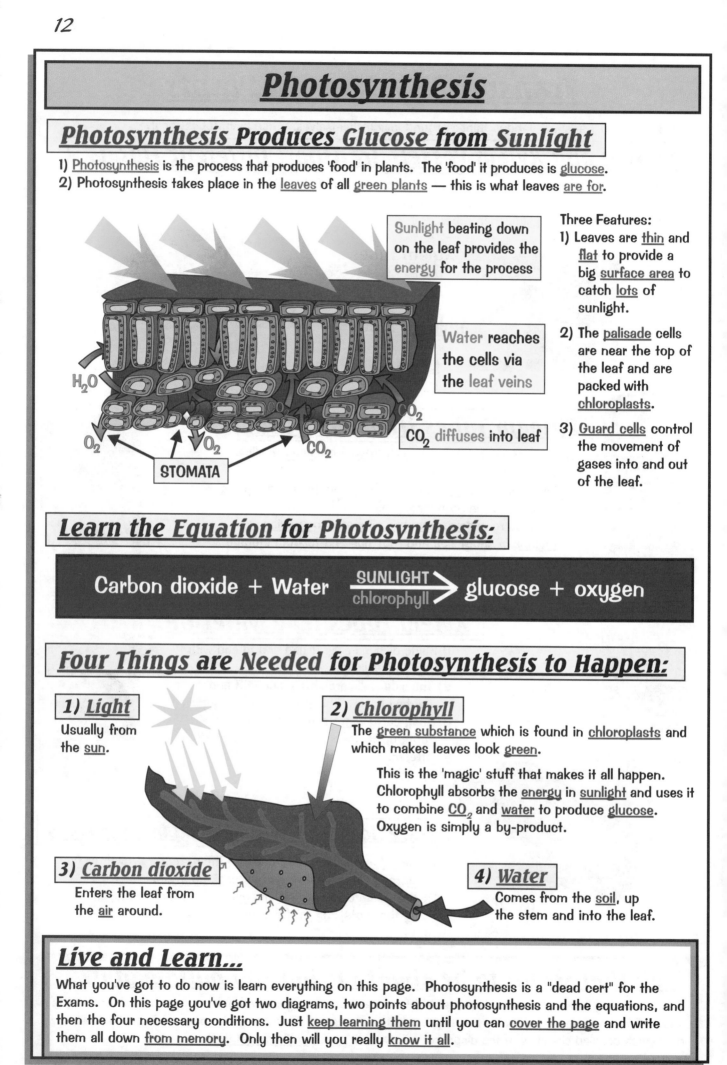

Sunlight beating down on the leaf provides the energy for the process

Water reaches the cells via the leaf veins

H_2O

CO_2 diffuses into leaf

O_2

O_2

CO_2

STOMATA

Three Features:

1) Leaves are <u>thin</u> and <u>flat</u> to provide a big <u>surface area</u> to catch <u>lots</u> of sunlight.

2) The <u>palisade</u> cells are near the top of the leaf and are packed with <u>chloroplasts</u>.

3) <u>Guard cells</u> control the movement of gases into and out of the leaf.

Learn the Equation for Photosynthesis:

$$\text{Carbon dioxide} + \text{Water} \xrightarrow[\text{chlorophyll}]{\text{SUNLIGHT}} \text{glucose} + \text{oxygen}$$

Four Things are Needed for Photosynthesis to Happen:

1) Light
Usually from the <u>sun</u>.

2) Chlorophyll
The <u>green substance</u> which is found in <u>chloroplasts</u> and which makes leaves look <u>green</u>.

This is the 'magic' stuff that makes it all happen. Chlorophyll absorbs the <u>energy</u> in <u>sunlight</u> and uses it to combine <u>CO_2</u> and <u>water</u> to produce <u>glucose</u>. Oxygen is simply a by-product.

3) Carbon dioxide
Enters the leaf from the <u>air</u> around.

4) Water
Comes from the <u>soil</u>, up the stem and into the leaf.

Live and Learn...

What you've got to do now is learn everything on this page. Photosynthesis is a "dead cert" for the Exams. On this page you've got two diagrams, two points about photosynthesis and the equations, and then the four necessary conditions. Just <u>keep learning them</u> until you can <u>cover the page</u> and write them all down <u>from memory</u>. Only then will you really <u>know it all</u>.

Altering the Rate of Photosynthesis

The Rate of Photosynthesis is affected by THREE factors

At any given time one or other of the following <u>three factors</u> will be the <u>limiting factor</u> which is keeping the photosynthesis <u>down</u> at the rate it is.

1) Not Enough LIGHT Slows Down the Rate of Photosynthesis

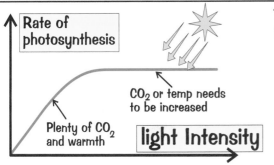

Rate of photosynthesis

CO_2 or temp needs to be increased

Plenty of CO_2 and warmth

light Intensity

The <u>chlorophyll</u> uses <u>light energy</u> to perform photosynthesis. It can only do it as fast as the light energy is arriving.

1) As the <u>light level</u> is raised, the rate of photosynthesis increases steadily but only up to a certain point.

2) Beyond that, it won't make any <u>difference</u> because then it'll be either the <u>temperature</u> or the <u>CO_2</u> level which is the limiting factor.

Chlorophyll actually only absorbs the <u>red</u> and <u>blue</u> ends of the <u>visible</u> light spectrum, but not the <u>green</u> <u>light</u> in the middle, which is <u>reflected</u> back. This is why the plant looks green.

2) Too Little CARBON DIOXIDE also Slows it Down

<u>CO_2</u> and <u>water</u> are the <u>raw materials</u>. Water is never really in short supply in a plant but only <u>0.03%</u> of the air around is CO_2 so it's actually pretty scarce as far as plants are concerned.

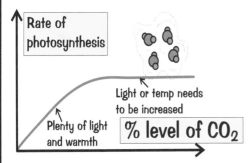

Rate of photosynthesis

Light or temp needs to be increased

Plenty of light and warmth

% level of CO_2

1) As with light intensity the amount of <u>CO_2</u> will only increase the rate of photosynthesis up to a point. After this the graph *flattens out* showing that CO_2 is no longer the <u>limiting factor</u>.

2) As long as <u>light</u> and <u>CO_2</u> are in plentiful supply then the factor limiting photosynthesis must be <u>temperature</u>.

3) The TEMPERATURE has to be Just Right

<u>Chlorophyll</u> is like an <u>enzyme</u> in that it works best when it's <u>warm</u> but not <u>too hot</u>. The rate of photosynthesis depends on how 'happy' the chlorophyll is: <u>warm</u> but not too hot.

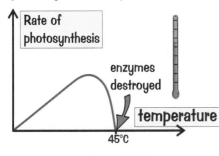

Rate of photosynthesis

enzymes destroyed

temperature

45°C

1) Note that you can't really have <u>too much</u> light or CO_2. The <u>temperature</u> however must <u>not</u> get too high or it <u>destroys</u> the chlorophyll enzymes.

2) This happens at about 45°C (which is pretty hot for outdoors, though greenhouses can get that hot if you're not careful).

3) <u>Usually</u>, though, if the temperature is the <u>limiting factor</u> it's because it's <u>too low</u>, and things need warming up a bit.

Revision — life isn't all fun and sunshine...

There are three limiting factors, a graph for each and an explanation of why the graphs level off or stop abruptly. <u>Cover the page</u> and practise <u>recalling all these details</u>, until you can do it.

Photosynthesis and Respiration

Photosynthesis and Respiration are OPPOSITE Processes:

1) Remember that photosynthesis in plants provides the food for all animals.
Plants trap the Sun's energy and turn it into glucose, which is basically stored chemical energy.
Animals along the food chain then use that energy in respiration to live and grow.
Without plants, all animals would die.

2) Respiration uses up oxygen and glucose and turns it back into carbon dioxide and water.

The EQUATIONS are the same but in opposite directions:

Photosynthesis: carbon dioxide + water → glucose + oxygen   (Requires Energy)

Respiration: glucose + oxygen → carbon dioxide + water   (Energy released)

Enclosed Plants: O_2 and CO_2 monitored over 24 hour cycles

In daylight (or any other light, except green) plants do photosynthesis and produce oxygen (and glucose).
But both plants and animals do respiration all the time, day and night, which uses up the oxygen and
releases carbon dioxide.   An experiment can be done to demonstrate this:

1) The level of oxygen will rise in the daytime due to photosynthesis producing more oxygen than the
plant's respiration uses up. At night the level of oxygen will fall because the plant's respiration will use it
up, and none is being produced. However, over a period of time the level of oxygen will slowly rise.

2) The level of carbon dioxide will fall during the daytime (used up by photosynthesis) and will rise at night
(produced by respiration). Over a period of time the level of CO_2 will fall steadily because plants
obviously use up more CO_2 than they produce. (Otherwise our atmosphere would still be full of carbon
dioxide like it was billions of years ago.)

Animals in there too could make the CO_2 level rise

It depends on the relative sizes of the plants and animals of course, but basically over a period of time the
level of O_2 could now fall, and the level of CO_2 could rise if there's too much "animal" compared to
"plant". The 24 hour pattern of up and down would still be similar though.

How do you learn all that lot then?...

At first sight this looks quite a tricky page to learn. In fact it's not that bad. The top half of the page
shows how photosynthesis and respiration are the reverse of each other, and the bottom half looks at
how the levels of oxygen and CO_2 vary over periods of 24 hours or longer.   With that basic structure in
mind you can cover the page and try to scribble it all down. It's really not that difficult.

How Plants Use The Glucose

1) Plants manufacture <u>glucose</u> in their <u>leaves</u>.
2) They then use some of the glucose initially for <u>respiration</u>.
3) This releases <u>energy</u> which enables them to <u>convert</u> the rest of the glucose into various other useful substances which they can use to build <u>new cells</u> and <u>grow</u>.
4) To produce some of these substances they also need to <u>gather</u> a few <u>minerals</u> from the soil.

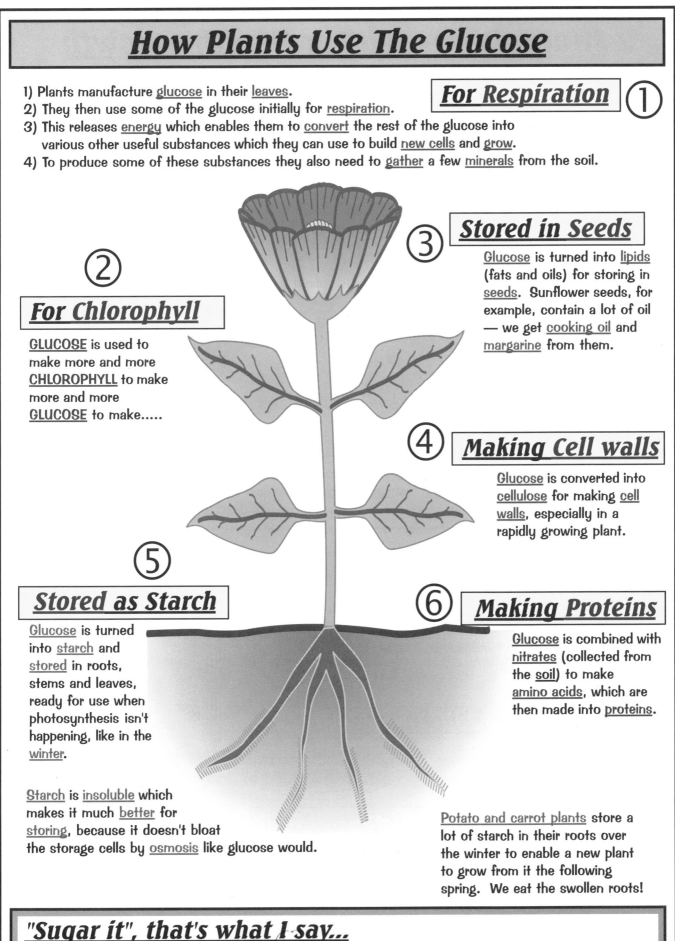

For Respiration ①

③ Stored in Seeds

<u>Glucose</u> is turned into <u>lipids</u> (fats and oils) for storing in <u>seeds</u>. Sunflower seeds, for example, contain a lot of oil — we get <u>cooking oil</u> and <u>margarine</u> from them.

② For Chlorophyll

<u>GLUCOSE</u> is used to make more and more <u>CHLOROPHYLL</u> to make more and more <u>GLUCOSE</u> to make.....

④ Making Cell walls

<u>Glucose</u> is converted into <u>cellulose</u> for making <u>cell walls</u>, especially in a rapidly growing plant.

⑤ Stored as Starch

<u>Glucose</u> is turned into <u>starch</u> and <u>stored</u> in roots, stems and leaves, ready for use when photosynthesis isn't happening, like in the <u>winter</u>.

<u>Starch</u> is <u>insoluble</u> which makes it much <u>better</u> for <u>storing</u>, because it doesn't bloat the storage cells by <u>osmosis</u> like glucose would.

⑥ Making Proteins

<u>Glucose</u> is combined with <u>nitrates</u> (collected from the <u>soil</u>) to make <u>amino acids</u>, which are then made into <u>proteins</u>.

<u>Potato and carrot plants</u> store a lot of starch in their roots over the winter to enable a new plant to grow from it the following spring. We eat the swollen roots!

"Sugar it", that's what I say...

There are six things that plants do with glucose. Can you spot them? If so, <u>learn them</u>, <u>cover the page</u>, and then display your new-found knowledge. In other words, sketch out the diagram and <u>scribble down</u> the six ways that plants use glucose, including all the extra details.

Minerals Needed For Healthy Growth

For <u>healthy</u> *growth* plants need these three really important mineral ions which they can only obtain from the <u>soil</u> through their <u>roots</u>:

The Three Essential Minerals

1) Nitrates

— for making <u>amino acids</u> and for the "synthesis" (making) of <u>proteins</u>.

2) Phosphates

— have an important role in reactions involved in <u>photosynthesis</u> and <u>respiration</u>.

3) Potassium

— helps the <u>enzymes</u> involved in <u>photosynthesis</u> and <u>respiration</u> to work.

Iron and Magnesium are also needed in Small Amounts

The three main minerals are needed in fairly large amounts, but there are other elements which are needed in much smaller amounts. <u>Iron</u> and <u>magnesium</u> are the most significant as they're required for making chlorophyll, which is pretty important to plants, in case you didn't know.

Lack of These Nutrients Causes Deficiency Symptoms:

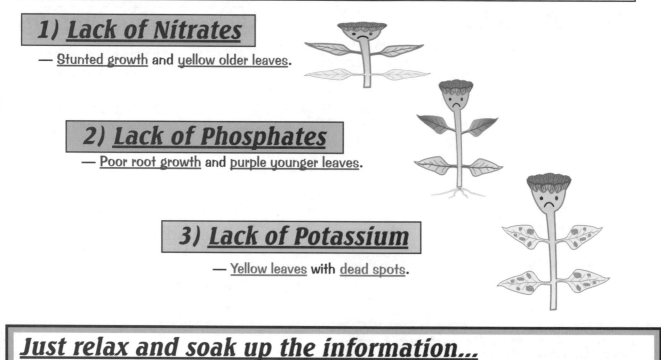

1) Lack of Nitrates

— <u>Stunted growth</u> and <u>yellow older leaves</u>.

2) Lack of Phosphates

— <u>Poor root growth</u> and <u>purple younger leaves</u>.

3) Lack of Potassium

— <u>Yellow leaves</u> with <u>dead spots</u>.

Just relax and soak up the information...

Very straightforward learning here. Two nice big clear sections with all the important bits highlighted in colour as usual. You should be able to <u>cover this page</u> and <u>scribble</u> virtually the whole thing down again with very little bother. <u>Learn and enjoy</u>.

Growth Hormones in Plants

Auxins are Plant Growth Hormones

1) Auxins are hormones which control growth at the tips of shoots and roots.
2) Auxin is produced in the tips and diffuses backwards to stimulate the cell elongation process which occurs in the cells just behind the tips.
3) If the tip of a shoot is removed, no auxin will be available and the shoot may stop growing.
4) Shoot tips also produce substances which inhibit the growth of side shoots. If the tips are removed it can result in a lot of side shoots because the inhibitor substance is no longer present. Hence, hedge clipping promotes bushier hedges, because it produces lots of side shoots.

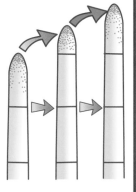

Auxins Change The Direction of Root and Shoot Growth

Extra auxin promotes growth in the shoot but actually inhibits growth in the root, — but this produces the desired result in both cases. Go figure (as Americans might say).

1) Shoots bend towards the light

1) When a shoot tip is exposed to light, it provides more auxin on the side that is in the shade than the side which is in the light.
2) This causes the shoot to grow faster on the shaded side and it bends towards the light.

2) Shoots bend away from Gravity

1) When a shoot finds itself growing sideways, the gravity produces an unequal distribution of auxin in the tip, with more auxin on the lower side.
2) This causes the lower side to grow faster, thus bending the shoot upwards.

gravity   gravity

3) Roots bend towards Gravity

1) A root growing sideways will experience the same redistribution of auxin to the lower side.
2) But in a root the extra auxin actually inhibits growth, causing it to bend downwards instead.

gravity   gravity

4) Roots bend towards Moisture

1) An uneven degree of moisture either side of a root will cause more auxin to appear on the side with more moisture.
2) This inhibits growth on that side, causing the root to grow in that direction, towards the moisture.

moisture   moisture

Just A Few Tips for Your Revision...

An easy page to learn. Just four points on auxins, together with a diagram, and then four ways that shoots and roots change direction, with a diagram for each. You just have to learn it. Then cover the page and scribble down the main points from memory. Then try again, and again...

Commercial Use of Plant Hormones

Plant hormones have a lot of uses in the <u>food growing business</u>.

1) Producing Seedless Fruit

1) Fruits normally only grow on plants which have been <u>pollinated</u> by insects, with the inevitable <u>seeds</u> in the middle of the fruit. If the plant <u>doesn't</u> get pollinated, the fruits and seeds don't grow.
2) However, if <u>growth hormones</u> are applied to <u>unpollinated flowers</u> the <u>fruits will grow</u> but the <u>seeds won't</u>!
3) This is great. Seedless satsumas and seedless grapes are just <u>so much nicer</u> than the 'natural' ones full of pips!

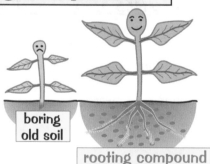

Hmmph!

(Redundant bee)

Unpollinated flower

Wonderful seedless grapes

2) Controlling the Ripening of Fruit

1) The <u>ripening</u> of fruits can be controlled either while they are still on the plant, or during <u>transport</u> to the shops.
2) This allows the fruit to be picked while it's still <u>unripe</u> (and therefore firmer and <u>less easily damaged</u>).
3) It can then be sprayed with <u>ripening hormone</u> and it will ripen on the way to the supermarket to be perfect just as it reaches the shelves.

3) Growing from Cuttings with Rooting Compound

1) A <u>cutting</u> is part of a plant that has been <u>cut off it</u>, like the end of a branch with a few leaves on it.
2) Normally, if you stick cuttings in the soil they <u>won't grow</u>, but if you add <u>rooting compound</u>, which is a plant <u>growth hormone</u>, they will produce roots rapidly and start growing as <u>new plants</u>.
3) This enables growers to produce lots of <u>clones</u> (exact copies) of a really good plant <u>very quickly</u>.

boring old soil

rooting compound

4) Killing Weeds

1) Most weeds growing in fields of crops or in a lawn are <u>broad-leaved</u>, in contrast to grass which has very <u>narrow leaves</u>.
2) <u>Selective weedkillers</u> have been developed from <u>plant growth hormones</u> which only affect the broad-leaved plants.
3) They totally disrupt their normal growth patterns, which soon <u>kills</u> them, whilst leaving the grass untouched.

Unhappy weeds

Remember, serious learning always bears fruit...

Another blissfully easy page. Just make sure you learn enough about each bit to answer a 3 mark Exam question on it (that means being able to make 3 valid points). As usual the sections are split into numbered points to help you remember them. They've all got three points to learn.
<u>So learn them</u>. Then <u>cover the page</u> and <u>scribble down</u> the 3 points for each . And tell me this:
— if you can't do it now, what makes you think it'll all suddenly "come back to you" in the Exam?

Revision Summary For Section Two

Jeepers creepers. Well, it's a pretty short section, but it still all needs learning.
It makes things a lot quicker if you make good use of all the pictures — these are far easier to
remember than just lists and lists of facts. Once you know the pictures, try to tag on the extra info
you need to know. You'll soon find that simply drawing the picture brings all the detail back to you.
Same drill as usual with these questions — keep going 'til you know the lot.

1) Sketch a typical plant and label the five important parts. Explain exactly what each bit does.

2) Sketch the cross-section of a leaf with seven labels. What is the leaf for?

3) Give five written details about the leaf structure in relation to what the leaf needs to do.

4) Explain what stomata do and how they do it.

5) What is transpiration? What causes it? What benefits does it bring?

6) What are the four factors which affect the rate of transpiration?

7) What is turgor pressure? How does it come about and what use is it to plants?

8) What are the two types of tubes in plants? Whereabouts are they found in plants?

9) List three features for both types of tube and sketch them both.

10) Sketch a root and say what goes on in the tubes inside it.

11) What does photosynthesis do? Where does it do it?

12) Write down the word equation for photosynthesis.

13) Sketch a leaf and show the four things needed for photosynthesis.

14) What are the three variable quantities which affect the rate of photosynthesis?

15) Sketch a graph for each one and explain the shape.

16) Describe conditions where each of the three factors is in short supply.

17) What's the relationship between photosynthesis and respiration?

18) Write down the two equations, and say which way the energy goes in each one.

19) Describe an experiment to demonstrate the interplay between photosynthesis and
    respiration. Sketch the graphs and explain their shape. What is the effect of animals?

20) Sketch a plant and label the six ways that plants use glucose.

21) Give a couple of extra details for each of the six uses.

22) List the five main minerals needed for healthy plant growth, and what they're needed for.

23) What are the three deficiency symptoms?

24) What are auxins? Where are they produced? What happens if you cut a shoot tip off?

25) There are four ways that auxins affect roots and shoots. Give full details for all four.

26) List the four commercial uses for plant hormones. How are seedless grapes made?

27) Explain what rooting compound is used for. How do hormonal weed killers work?

The Digestive System

You'll definitely get a question on this in your Exam so take your time and learn this very important diagram in all its infinite glory. And that includes the words too:

Ten Bits of Your Grisly Digestive System to Learn:

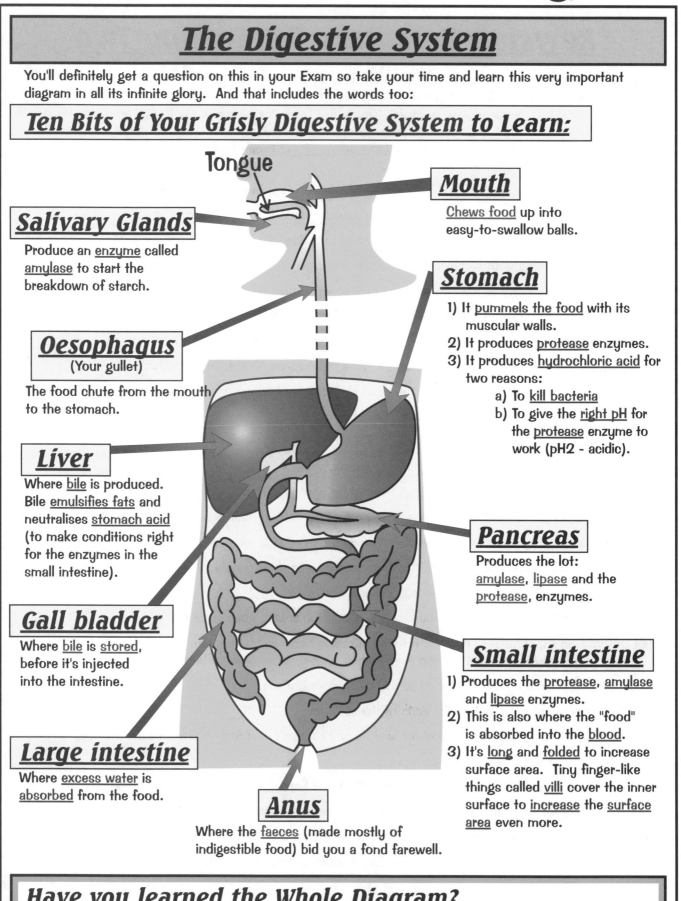

Tongue

Mouth
Chews food up into easy-to-swallow balls.

Salivary Glands
Produce an enzyme called amylase to start the breakdown of starch.

Stomach
1) It pummels the food with its muscular walls.
2) It produces protease enzymes.
3) It produces hydrochloric acid for two reasons:
    a) To kill bacteria
    b) To give the right pH for the protease enzyme to work (pH2 - acidic).

Oesophagus
(Your gullet)

The food chute from the mouth to the stomach.

Liver
Where bile is produced. Bile emulsifies fats and neutralises stomach acid (to make conditions right for the enzymes in the small intestine).

Pancreas
Produces the lot: amylase, lipase and the protease, enzymes.

Gall bladder
Where bile is stored, before it's injected into the intestine.

Small intestine
1) Produces the protease, amylase and lipase enzymes.
2) This is also where the "food" is absorbed into the blood.
3) It's long and folded to increase surface area. Tiny finger-like things called villi cover the inner surface to increase the surface area even more.

Large intestine
Where excess water is absorbed from the food.

Anus
Where the faeces (made mostly of indigestible food) bid you a fond farewell.

Have you learned the Whole Diagram?
The one thing they won't ask you to do in the Exam is draw the whole thing out yourself. BUT they will ask you about any part of it, e.g. "What is the position of the liver?", or "What does the pancreas produce?", or "What is the function of bile?" So in the end you have to learn the whole thing anyway. And that means being able to cover the page and draw it out, words and all. If you can't draw it all out from memory — then you haven't learnt it. Simple as that.

Digestive System Extras

All the Way Along there's Muscular and Glandular Tissue

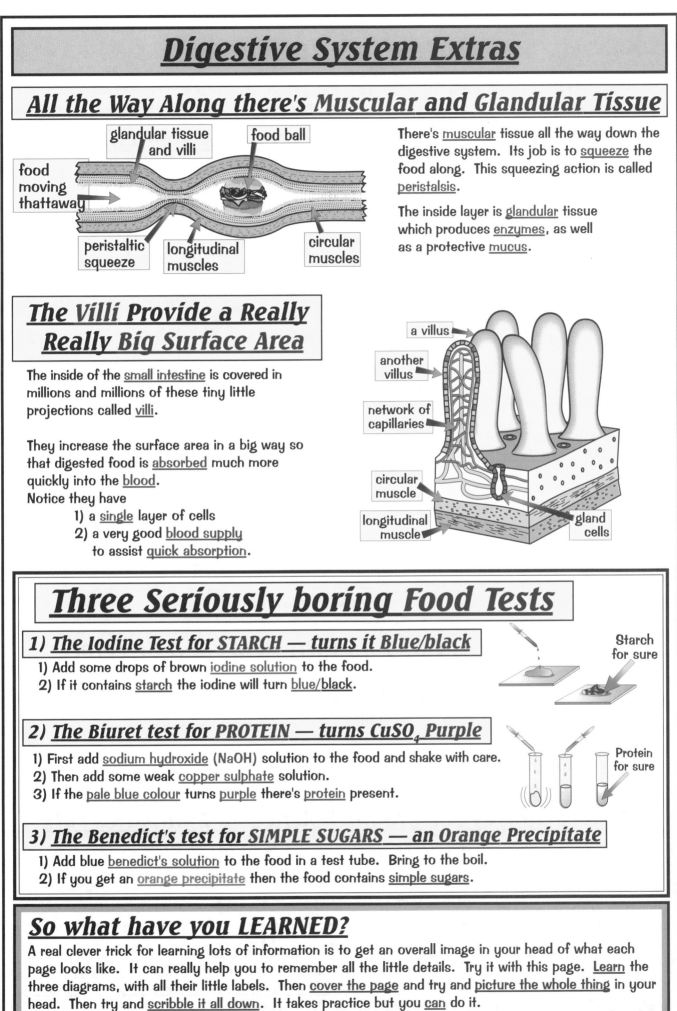

glandular tissue and villi

food ball

food moving thattaway

peristaltic squeeze

longitudinal muscles

circular muscles

There's <u>muscular</u> tissue all the way down the digestive system. Its job is to <u>squeeze</u> the food along. This squeezing action is called <u>peristalsis</u>.

The inside layer is <u>glandular</u> tissue which produces <u>enzymes</u>, as well as a protective <u>mucus</u>.

The Villi Provide a Really Really Big Surface Area

The inside of the <u>small intestine</u> is covered in millions and millions of these tiny little projections called <u>villi</u>.

They increase the surface area in a big way so that digested food is <u>absorbed</u> much more quickly into the <u>blood</u>.
Notice they have
    1) a <u>single</u> layer of cells
    2) a very good <u>blood supply</u>
        to assist <u>quick absorption</u>.

a villus

another villus

network of capillaries

circular muscle

longitudinal muscle

gland cells

Three Seriously boring Food Tests

1) The Iodine Test for STARCH — turns it Blue/black

1) Add some drops of brown <u>iodine solution</u> to the food.
2) If it contains <u>starch</u> the iodine will turn <u>blue/black</u>.

Starch for sure

2) The Biuret test for PROTEIN — turns $CuSO_4$ Purple

1) First add <u>sodium hydroxide</u> (NaOH) solution to the food and shake with care.
2) Then add some weak <u>copper sulphate</u> solution.
3) If the <u>pale blue colour</u> turns <u>purple</u> there's <u>protein</u> present.

Protein for sure

3) The Benedict's test for SIMPLE SUGARS — an Orange Precipitate

1) Add blue <u>benedict's solution</u> to the food in a test tube. Bring to the boil.
2) If you get an <u>orange precipitate</u> then the food contains <u>simple sugars</u>.

So what have you LEARNED?

A real clever trick for learning lots of information is to get an overall image in your head of what each page looks like. It can really help you to remember all the little details. Try it with this page. <u>Learn</u> the three diagrams, with all their little labels. Then <u>cover the page</u> and try and <u>picture the whole thing</u> in your head. Then try and <u>scribble it all down</u>. It takes practice but you <u>can</u> do it.

Digestive Enzymes

There are only <u>three</u> main digestive enzymes. Sadly they all have silly names that can be hard to learn and their '"products of digestion" all have suitably silly names too. Ah well — that's Biology for you!

Enzymes break down Big Molecules into Small Ones

1) <u>Starch</u>, <u>proteins</u> and <u>fats</u> are <u>big</u> molecules which can't pass through cell walls into the blood.
2) <u>Sugars</u>, <u>amino acids</u> and <u>fatty acids/glycerol</u> are <u>much smaller</u> molecules which can pass easily into the blood.
3) <u>Enzymes</u> act as <u>catalysts</u> to break down the <u>big molecules</u> into the <u>smaller ones</u>.

1) Amylase Converts Starch into Simple Sugars

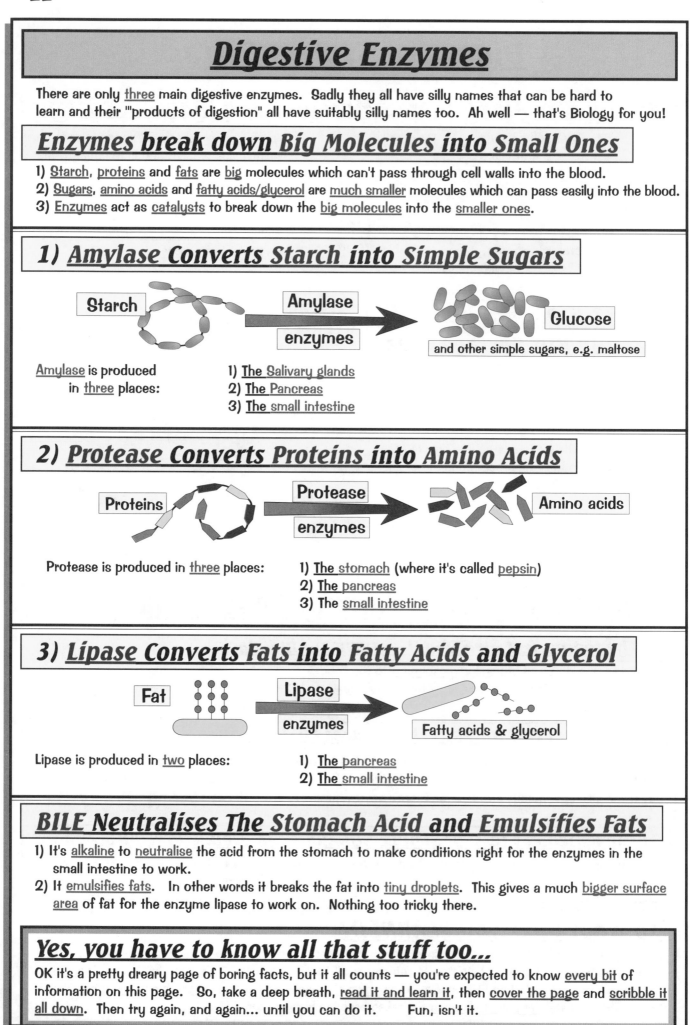

Starch → **Amylase enzymes** → **Glucose**

and other simple sugars, e.g. maltose

<u>Amylase</u> is produced in <u>three</u> places:
1) <u>The Salivary glands</u>
2) <u>The Pancreas</u>
3) <u>The small intestine</u>

2) Protease Converts Proteins into Amino Acids

Proteins → **Protease enzymes** → **Amino acids**

Protease is produced in <u>three</u> places:
1) <u>The stomach</u> (where it's called <u>pepsin</u>)
2) <u>The pancreas</u>
3) The <u>small intestine</u>

3) Lipase Converts Fats into Fatty Acids and Glycerol

Fat → **Lipase enzymes** → Fatty acids & glycerol

Lipase is produced in <u>two</u> places:
1) <u>The pancreas</u>
2) <u>The small intestine</u>

BILE Neutralises The Stomach Acid and Emulsifies Fats

1) It's <u>alkaline</u> to <u>neutralise</u> the acid from the stomach to make conditions right for the enzymes in the small intestine to work.
2) It <u>emulsifies fats</u>. In other words it breaks the fat into <u>tiny droplets</u>. This gives a much <u>bigger surface area</u> of fat for the enzyme lipase to work on. Nothing too tricky there.

Yes, you have to know all that stuff too...

OK it's a pretty dreary page of boring facts, but it all counts — you're expected to know <u>every bit</u> of information on this page. So, take a deep breath, <u>read it and learn it</u>, then <u>cover the page</u> and <u>scribble it all down</u>. Then try again, and again... until you can do it. Fun, isn't it.

Diffusion of "Food" Molecules

The Big Food Molecules Must First be Broken Down

After you've chewed your food up and your stomach's had its turn at munching it up still further, it's still made up of quite big molecules, namely: Starch, Proteins and Fats.

These are still too big to diffuse into the blood, and so they are broken down in the small intestine into smaller molecules: glucose, amino acids, fatty acids and glycerol.

| Bread / potatoes / muesli | Starch | Glucose molecules |

| Meat / eggs / fish | Proteins | Amino acids |

| Butter / cooking oil / sausages | Fat | Fatty acids and glycerol molecules |

The Small Molecules Can Then Diffuse into the Blood

① These molecules (glucose, amino acids, fatty acids and glycerol) are then small enough to diffuse into the blood.

③ They then travel to where they're needed, and then diffuse out again. It's all clever stuff.

② When the blood has loads of nutrients in it, the molecules will only "diffuse" into the blood with the help of active uptake because the concentration gradient is the wrong way.

Inside the gut

blood flows from gut to body cells

The small molecules diffuse into the blood...

..and then out again somewhere else...

Let's see what you've LEARNED, shall we...

Practise answering these three questions until you can do them all without looking at the page. If you can't, then it means just one thing — you haven't learnt it. (Pretty obviously)

1) Name the three big molecules that won't diffuse into the blood.
2) Name the four small molecules that will diffuse into the blood.

The Circulatory System

The circulatory system's main function is to get food and oxygen to every cell in the body. The diagram shows the basic layout, but make sure you learn the five important points too.

The DOUBLE Circulatory System, actually

The <u>heart</u> is actually <u>two pumps</u>. The <u>right side</u> pumps deoxygenated blood to the <u>lungs</u> to <u>collect oxygen</u>. Then the <u>left side</u> pumps this oxygenated blood <u>around the body</u>.

① ②

Arteries carry blood <u>away from the heart</u> at <u>high pressure</u>.

③

Normally, arteries carry <u>oxygenated blood</u> and veins carry <u>deoxygenated blood</u>.

The <u>pulmonary artery</u> and <u>pulmonary vein</u> are the <u>big exceptions</u> to this rule (see diagram).

④

The arteries eventually split off into thousands of tiny <u>capillaries</u> which take blood to <u>every cell</u> in the body.

⑤

The <u>veins</u> then collect the <u>"used" blood</u> and carry it <u>back to the heart</u> at <u>low pressure</u> to be pumped round again.

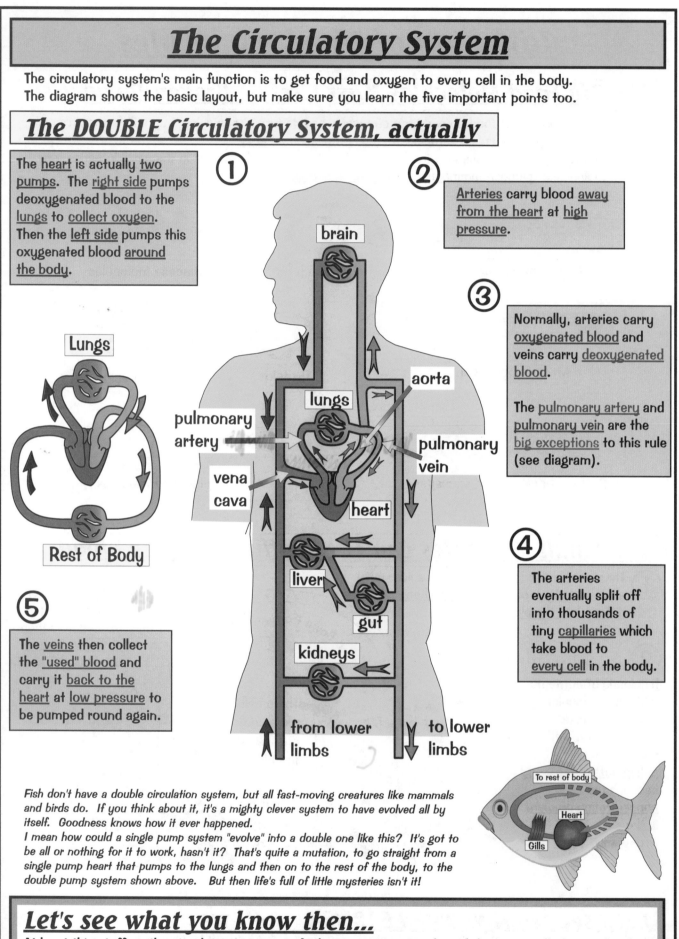

Lungs

Rest of Body

brain

pulmonary artery

lungs

aorta

pulmonary vein

vena cava

heart

liver

gut

kidneys

from lower limbs

to lower limbs

To rest of body

Heart

Gills

Fish don't have a double circulation system, but all fast-moving creatures like mammals and birds do. If you think about it, it's a mighty clever system to have evolved all by itself. Goodness knows how it ever happened.
I mean how could a single pump system "evolve" into a double one like this? It's got to be all or nothing for it to work, hasn't it? That's quite a mutation, to go straight from a single pump heart that pumps to the lungs and then on to the rest of the body, to the double pump system shown above. But then life's full of little mysteries isn't it!

Let's see what you know then...

At least this stuff on the circulatory system is fairly interesting. Mind you, there are still plenty of picky little details you need to be clear about. And yes, you've guessed it, there's one surefire way to check just how clear you are — <u>read it, learn it, then cover the page and reproduce it</u>.
Having to sketch the diagram out again <u>from memory</u> is the only way to <u>really learn it</u>.

Blood Vessels

There are three different types of blood vessel and you need to know all about them:

Arteries Carry Blood Under Pressure

1) <u>Arteries</u> carry oxygenated blood <u>away</u> from the heart.
2) It comes out of the heart at <u>high pressure</u>, so the artery walls have to be <u>strong</u> and <u>elastic</u>.
3) Note how <u>thick</u> the walls are compared to the size of the hole down the middle (the "lumen" — silly name!)

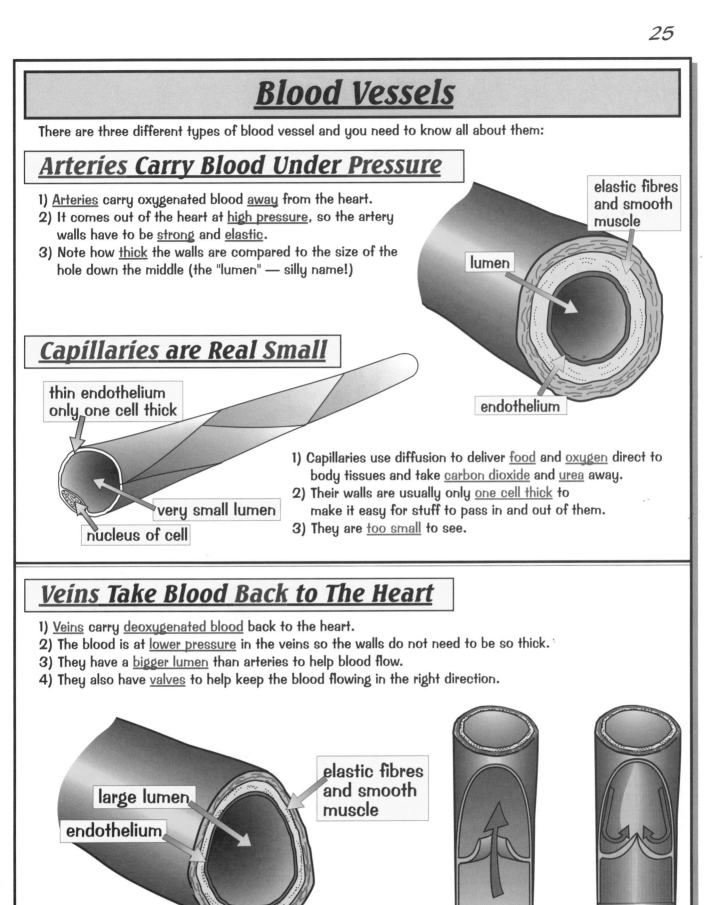

elastic fibres and smooth muscle

lumen

endothelium

Capillaries are Real Small

thin endothelium only one cell thick

very small lumen

nucleus of cell

1) Capillaries use diffusion to deliver <u>food</u> and <u>oxygen</u> direct to body tissues and take <u>carbon dioxide</u> and <u>urea</u> away.
2) Their walls are usually only <u>one cell thick</u> to make it easy for stuff to pass in and out of them.
3) They are <u>too small</u> to see.

Veins Take Blood Back to The Heart

1) <u>Veins</u> carry <u>deoxygenated blood</u> back to the heart.
2) The blood is at <u>lower pressure</u> in the veins so the walls do not need to be so thick.
3) They have a <u>bigger lumen</u> than arteries to help blood flow.
4) They also have <u>valves</u> to help keep the blood flowing in the right direction.

large lumen

elastic fibres and smooth muscle

endothelium

Don't struggle in Vain...

Let's face it these are mighty easy diagrams to learn. Just make sure you learn the numbered points as well. I reckon it can't take more than two or three attempts before you can scribble out the whole of this page, diagrams and all, <u>entirely from memory</u>. <u>Concentrate on learning the bits you forgot each time</u>, of course. Try it and see how right I am!

The Heart

The heart is made almost entirely of <u>muscle</u>. And it's a <u>double pump</u>.
Visualise this diagram with its bigger side full of red, <u>oxygenated blood</u>, and
its smaller side full of blue, <u>deoxygenated blood</u>, and learn that the <u>left side</u> is <u>bigger</u>.

Learn This Diagram of the Heart with All its Labels

Right Side   Left Side

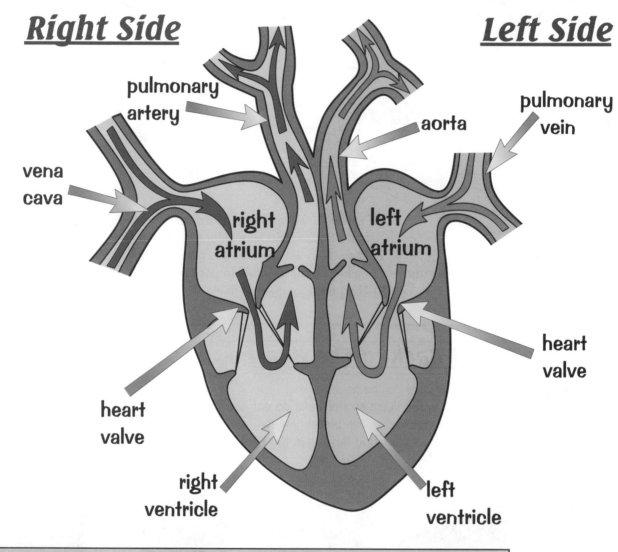

pulmonary
artery

aorta

pulmonary
vein

vena
cava

right
atrium

left
atrium

heart
valve

heart
valve

right
ventricle

left
ventricle

Four Extra Details to Delight and Thrill You

1) The <u>right side</u> of the heart receives <u>deoxygenated blood</u> from the body
   and pumps it only to the <u>lungs</u>, so it has <u>thinner walls</u> than the left side.

2) The <u>left side</u> receives <u>oxygenated blood</u> from the lungs and pumps it
   out round the <u>whole body</u>, so it has thicker, more <u>muscular walls</u>.

3) The ventricles are much <u>bigger</u> than the atria because they push blood <u>round the body</u>.

4) The <u>valves</u> are for preventing <u>backflow</u> of blood.

OK let's get to the Heart of the Matter...

They quite often put a diagram of the heart in the Exam and ask you to label parts of it.
There's only one way to be sure you can label it all and that's to learn the diagram until you can sketch it
out, with all the labels, <u>from memory</u>.   Also <u>learn</u> the four points at the bottom.

The Pumping Cycle

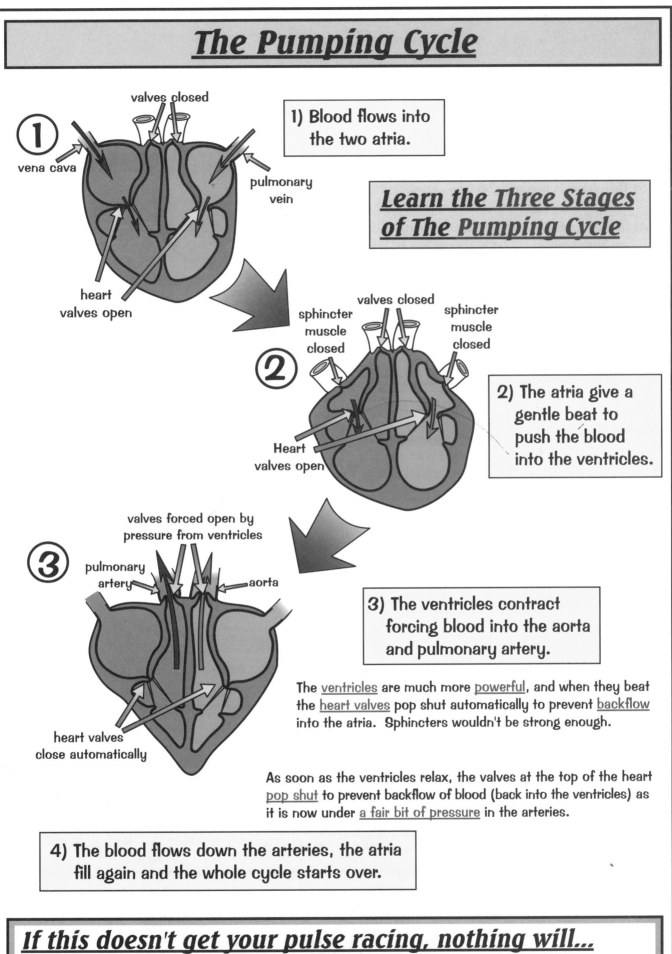

1) Blood flows into the two atria.

Learn the Three Stages of The Pumping Cycle

2) The atria give a gentle beat to push the blood into the ventricles.

3) The ventricles contract forcing blood into the aorta and pulmonary artery.

The ventricles are much more powerful, and when they beat the heart valves pop shut automatically to prevent backflow into the atria. Sphincters wouldn't be strong enough.

As soon as the ventricles relax, the valves at the top of the heart pop shut to prevent backflow of blood (back into the ventricles) as it is now under a fair bit of pressure in the arteries.

4) The blood flows down the arteries, the atria fill again and the whole cycle starts over.

If this doesn't get your pulse racing, nothing will...

You need to know the details of each step of the pumping cycle. They will quite cheerfully give you a diagram similar to one of the above and ask you which valves are open or where the blood is flowing etc. etc. Make sure you can sketch out all three diagrams from memory.

Blood

Red Blood Cells

1) Their job is to carry <u>oxygen</u> to all the cells in the body.

2) They have a flying doughnut shape to give <u>maximum</u> <u>surface area</u> for absorbing <u>oxygen</u>.

3) They contain <u>haemoglobin</u> when combined with oxygen which is very <u>red</u>, and which contains a lot of <u>iron</u>.

4) In the <u>lungs</u>, haemoglobin absorbs <u>oxygen</u> to become <u>oxyhaemoglobin</u>. In body tissues the reverse happens to release oxygen to the <u>cells</u>.

5) Red blood cells have no need for a <u>nucleus</u>, so they don't have one, making <u>more room</u> for haemoglobin.

White Blood Cells

1) Their main role is <u>defence</u> against <u>disease</u>.
2) They have a <u>big nucleus</u>.
3) They gobble up unwelcome <u>micro-organisms</u>.
4) They produce <u>antibodies</u> to fight bacteria.
5) They produce <u>antitoxins</u> to neutralise the toxins produced by bacteria.

Plasma

This is a pale straw-coloured liquid which <u>carries just about everything</u>:
1) <u>Red</u> and <u>white blood cells</u> and <u>platelets</u>.
2) Nutrients like <u>glucose</u> and <u>amino acids</u>.
3) <u>Carbon dioxide</u>.
4) <u>Urea</u>.
5) <u>Hormones</u>.
6) <u>Antibodies</u> and <u>antitoxins</u> produced by the white blood cells.

Platelets

1) These are <u>small fragments</u> of <u>cells</u>.
2) They have <u>no nucleus</u>.
3) They help the blood to <u>clot</u> at a wound. This stops all your <u>blood pouring out</u> and stops <u>micro organisms</u> getting in. (So basically they just float about waiting for accidents to happen!)

More Blood, Sweat and Tears...

Do the same as usual — learn the facts <u>until you can write them down from memory</u>.

Just in case you think all this formal learning is a waste of time, how do you think you'd get on with these typical Exam questions if you didn't <u>learn</u> it all first?

<u>Three typical Exam questions:</u>
1) What is the function of blood plasma? (4 marks)
2) What do white blood cells do? (3 marks)
3) What is the function of haemoglobin? (4 marks)

Lungs and Breathing

Instead of saying 'breathing', they sometimes call it 'ventilation' in the exams. Don't get confused with those big shiny metal things that Bruce Willis likes climbing through, it's just breathing, ok.

The Thorax

Learn this diagram real good.

1) The thorax is the top part of your 'body'.

2) The lungs are like big pink sponges.

3) The trachea splits into two tubes called 'bronchi' (each one is 'a bronchus'), one going to each lung.

4) The bronchi split into progressively smaller tubes called bronchioles.

5) The bronchioles finally end at small bags called alveoli where the gas exchange takes place.

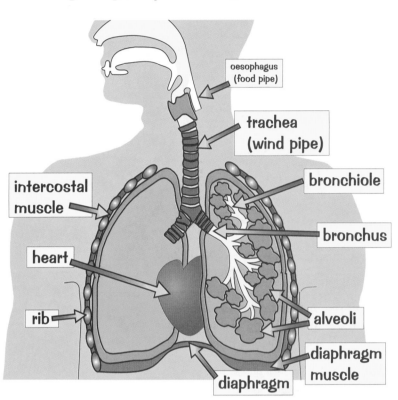

Breathing In...

1) Intercostals and diaphragm contract.
2) Thorax volume increases.
3) This decreases the pressure, drawing air in.

...and Breathing Out

1) Intercostals and diaphragm relax.
2) Thorax volume decreases.
3) Air is forced out.

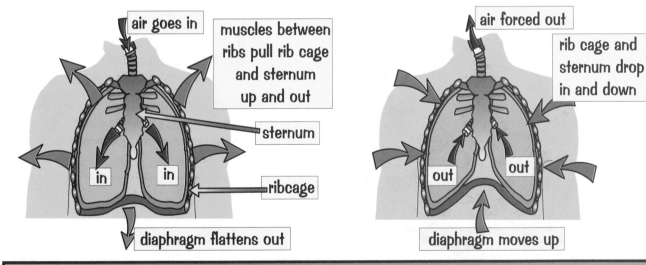

Stop Huffing and Puffing and just LEARN IT...

No dreary lists of facts this time anyway, just three splendid diagrams to learn.
When you practise repeating diagrams from memory, you don't have to draw them really neatly, just sketch them clearly enough to label all the important bits. They would never ask you to draw a really fancy diagram in the Exam, but they will expect you to label one. But the only way to be sure you really know a diagram is to sketch it and label it, all from memory.

Alveoli, Cells and Diffusion

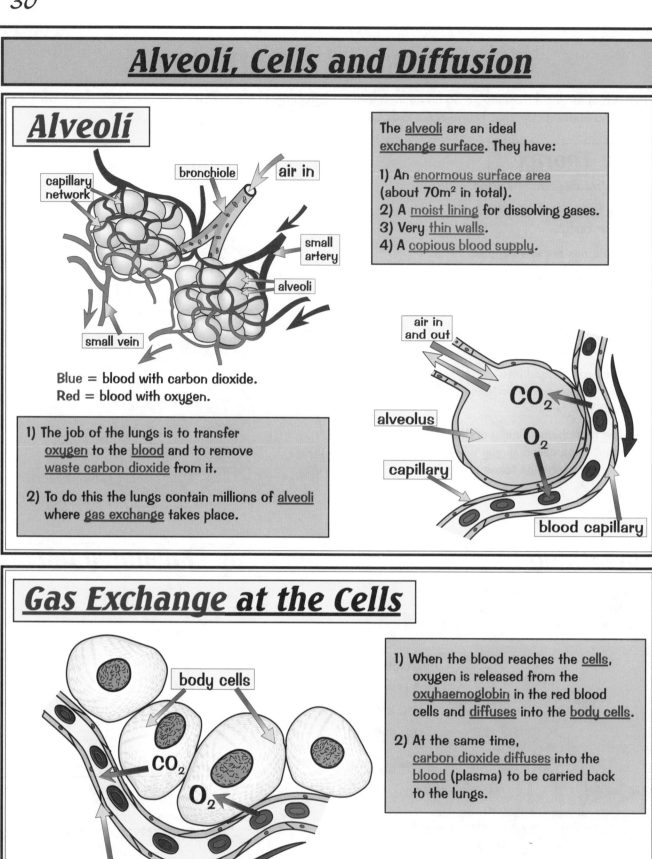

Alveoli

capillary network
bronchiole
air in
small artery
alveoli
small vein

Blue = blood with carbon dioxide.
Red = blood with oxygen.

The <u>alveoli</u> are an ideal
<u>exchange surface</u>. They have:

1) An <u>enormous surface area</u>
(about 70m² in total).
2) A <u>moist lining</u> for dissolving gases.
3) Very <u>thin walls</u>.
4) A <u>copious blood supply</u>.

1) The job of the lungs is to transfer
<u>oxygen</u> to the <u>blood</u> and to remove
<u>waste carbon dioxide</u> from it.

2) To do this the lungs contain millions of <u>alveoli</u>
where <u>gas exchange</u> takes place.

air in and out
CO_2
O_2
alveolus
capillary
blood capillary

Gas Exchange at the Cells

body cells
CO_2
O_2
blood capillary

1) When the blood reaches the <u>cells</u>,
oxygen is released from the
<u>oxyhaemoglobin</u> in the red blood
cells and <u>diffuses</u> into the <u>body cells</u>.

2) At the same time,
<u>carbon dioxide diffuses</u> into the
<u>blood</u> (plasma) to be carried back
to the lungs.

This is a very Easy Page To Learn...

Notice that the numbered points repeat information that the diagrams already show very clearly.
The big idea is that you should <u>understand and remember</u> what goes on and why it all works so well.
A clear visual image in your head of these diagrams makes it a lot easier.
<u>Learn</u> the diagrams, words and all, until you can sketch them out <u>entirely from memory</u>.

Respiration

Respiration is NOT "breathing in and out"

1) Respiration is NOT breathing in and breathing out, as you might think.
2) Respiration actually goes on in every cell in your body.
3) Respiration is the process of converting glucose to energy.
4) This energy is used to: build up larger molecules (like proteins)
   contract muscles
   maintain a steady body temperature
5) Plants respire too. All living things "respire". They convert food from light into energy.

RESPIRATION is the process of CONVERTING GLUCOSE TO ENERGY, which goes on IN EVERY CELL

Aerobic Respiration Needs Plenty of Oxygen

1) Aerobic respiration is what happens if there's plenty of oxygen available.
2) "Aerobic" just means "with oxygen" and it's the ideal way to convert glucose into energy.

You need to learn the word equation:

Glucose + Oxygen → Carbon Dioxide + Water + Energy

..and the chemical equation:

$$C_6H_{12}O_6 + 6O_2 \rightarrow 6CO_2 + 6H_2O + Energy$$

Composition of Inhaled and Exhaled Air

This is the difference between what you breathe in and what you breathe out:

GAS:	AIR IN:	AIR OUT:
Nitrogen	79%	79%
Oxygen	21%	17%
CO_2	0%	4%
Water vapour	Varies	Loads

1) The amount of oxygen used matches the amount of CO_2 produced, as in the above equation.

2) Notice that even with millions of alveoli, you still only absorb a small proportion of the oxygen in each breath.

One Big Deep Breath and LEARN IT...

There are three sections on this page and learning them well enough to scribble them down from memory isn't so difficult. Try to visualise the basic page layout and remember how many numbered points there are for each bit. You don't have to write it out word for word, just make sure you remember the important points.

Anaerobic Respiration — You and Yeast

Anaerobic Respiration doesn't use Oxygen at all

1) Anaerobic respiration is what happens if there's no oxygen available.

2) "Anaerobic" just means "without oxygen". It's the incomplete breakdown of glucose which is NOT the best way to convert glucose into energy because it produces lactic acid.

You need to learn the word equation:

$$\text{Glucose} \longrightarrow \text{Energy} + \text{Lactic Acid}$$

3) Anaerobic respiration does not produce nearly as much energy as aerobic respiration — but it's useful in emergencies.

Exercise and the Oxygen Debt

1) When you do vigorous exercise and your body can't supply enough oxygen to your muscles they start doing anaerobic respiration instead.

2) This isn't great because lactic acid builds up in the muscles, which gets painful.

3) The advantage is that at least you can keep on using your muscles for a while longer.

4) After resorting to anaerobic respiration, when you stop you'll have an oxygen debt.

5) In other words you have to "repay" the oxygen that you didn't get to your muscles in time, because your lungs, heart and blood couldn't keep up with the demand earlier on.

6) This means you have to keep breathing hard for a while after you stop to get oxygen into your muscles to oxidise the painful lactic acid to harmless CO_2 and water.

7) When high levels of CO_2 and lactic acid are detected in the blood (by the brain), the pulse and breathing rate are both increased automatically to try and rectify the situation.

8) A good measure of fitness is how quickly you can recover to normal breathing and pulse after doing some vigorous exercise. This is called your recovery time.

Anaerobic Respiration in Yeast Makes Ethanol

Ethanol is exactly the same thing as alcohol so Yeast is used to brew beer and other alcoholic drinks using anaerobic respiration. Another word for this process is fermentation. Learn this formula for it:

$$\text{Glucose} \longrightarrow \text{Ethanol} + \text{Carbon Dioxide} + \text{Energy}$$

In brewing, of course the alcohol's the most important bit, but the CO_2 also makes it kinda fizzy. (See the Chemistry Book for more details on fermentation.)

Let's see what you know then...

Read the page then see what you can scribble down about each of the three sections. Then try again. You don't want to try and learn those eight points about "Oxygen Debt" too formally. It's much better to write your own mini-essay on it and then see what stuff you missed. Enjoy.

The Nervous System

Sense Organs and Receptors

The Five Sense Organs and the stimuli that each one is sensitive to:

The five sense organs are:
Eyes ears nose tongue skin

These five different sense organs all contain different receptors.

Receptors are groups of cells which are sensitive to a stimulus such as light or heat, etc.

Sense organs and Receptors Don't get them mixed up:

The eye is a sense organ — it contains light receptors (rods and cones).
The ear is a sense organ — it contains sound-receptors.

Receptors are cells that turn energy (e.g. light energy) into electrical impulses.

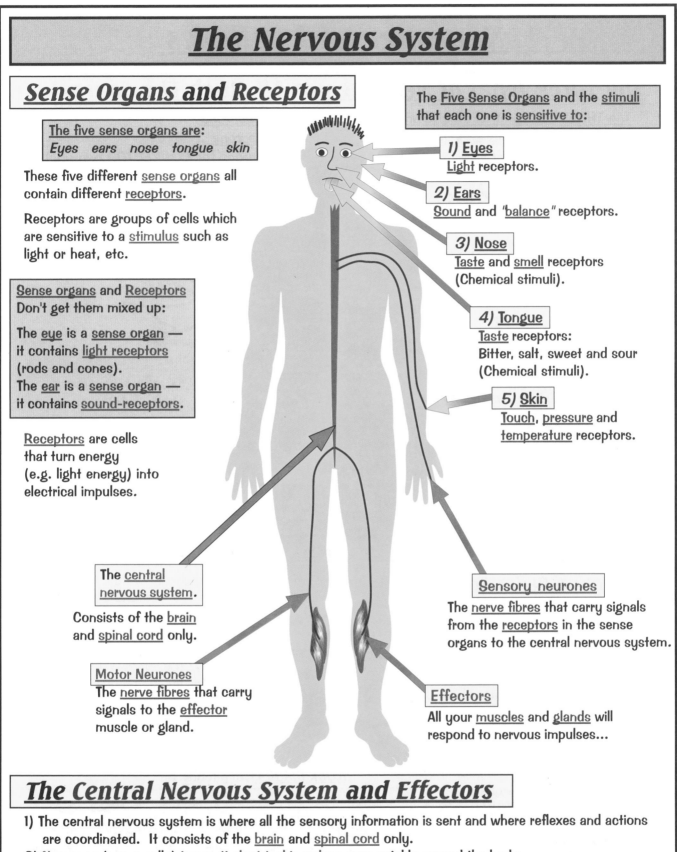

1) Eyes
Light receptors.

2) Ears
Sound and "balance" receptors.

3) Nose
Taste and smell receptors (Chemical stimuli).

4) Tongue
Taste receptors:
Bitter, salt, sweet and sour (Chemical stimuli).

5) Skin
Touch, pressure and temperature receptors.

Sensory neurones
The nerve fibres that carry signals from the receptors in the sense organs to the central nervous system.

The central nervous system.
Consists of the brain and spinal cord only.

Motor Neurones
The nerve fibres that carry signals to the effector muscle or gland.

Effectors
All your muscles and glands will respond to nervous impulses...

The Central Nervous System and Effectors

1) The central nervous system is where all the sensory information is sent and where reflexes and actions are coordinated. It consists of the brain and spinal cord only.
2) Neurones (nerve cells) transmit electrical impulses very quickly around the body.
3) The effectors are muscles and glands which respond to the various stimuli according to the instructions sent from the central nervous system.

This stuff is easy — I mean it's all just common senses...

There's quite a few names to learn here (as ever!).
But there's no drivel. It's all worth marks in the Exam, so learn it all.
Practise until you can cover the page and scribble down all the details from memory.

Neurones and Reflexes

The Three Types of Neurone are All Much The Same

The THREE TYPES of NEURONE are:

(They're all *pretty much the same*, they're just *connected to different things*, that's all.)

1) *SENSORY neurone*
2) *MOTOR neurone*
3) *RELAY neurone* (or *CONNECTOR neurone*).

A Typical Neurone: — *Learn the names* of all the bits:

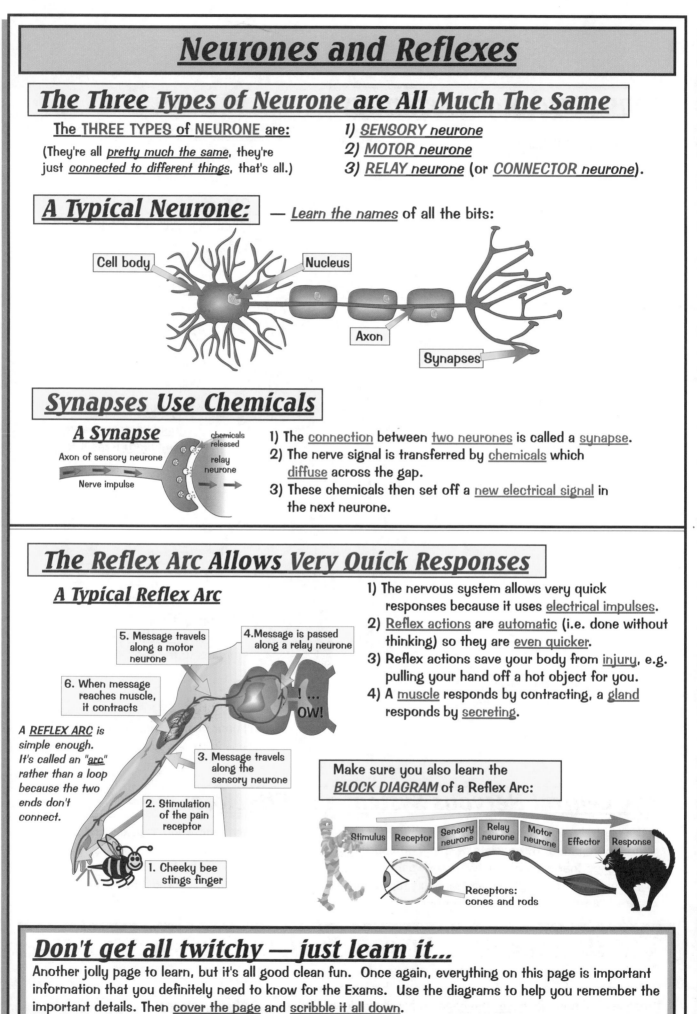

Cell body

Nucleus

Axon

Synapses

Synapses Use Chemicals

A Synapse

chemicals released

Axon of sensory neurone

relay neurone

Nerve impulse

1) The <u>connection</u> between <u>two neurones</u> is called a <u>synapse</u>.
2) The nerve signal is transferred by <u>chemicals</u> which <u>diffuse</u> across the gap.
3) These chemicals then set off a <u>new electrical signal</u> in the next neurone.

The Reflex Arc Allows Very Quick Responses

A Typical Reflex Arc

5. Message travels along a motor neurone

4. Message is passed along a relay neurone

6. When message reaches muscle, it contracts

! ... OW!

A REFLEX ARC is simple enough. It's called an "<u>arc</u>" rather than a loop because the two ends don't connect.

3. Message travels along the sensory neurone

2. Stimulation of the pain receptor

1. Cheeky bee stings finger

1) The nervous system allows very quick responses because it uses <u>electrical impulses</u>.
2) <u>Reflex actions</u> are <u>automatic</u> (i.e. done without thinking) so they are <u>even quicker</u>.
3) Reflex actions save your body from <u>injury</u>, e.g. pulling your hand off a hot object for you.
4) A <u>muscle</u> responds by contracting, a <u>gland</u> responds by <u>secreting</u>.

Make sure you also learn the *BLOCK DIAGRAM* of a Reflex Arc:

Stimulus | Receptor | Sensory neurone | Relay neurone | Motor neurone | Effector | Response

Receptors: cones and rods

Don't get all twitchy — just learn it...

Another jolly page to learn, but it's all good clean fun. Once again, everything on this page is important information that you definitely need to know for the Exams. Use the diagrams to help you remember the important details. Then <u>cover the page</u> and <u>scribble it all down</u>.

The Eye

Learn The Eye with all its labels:

1) The pupil is the hole in the middle of the iris, which the light goes through.
2) The eye is filled with a clear liquid which supports the spherical shape of the eye.
3) The retina is the light sensitive part and is covered in rods and cones which detect light.
4) Rods are more sensitive in dim light but only sense in black and white.
5) Cones are sensitive to colours but are not so good in dim light.
6) The fovea is a spot with loads of tightly packed cones which gives a really sharp image when you look straight at something.

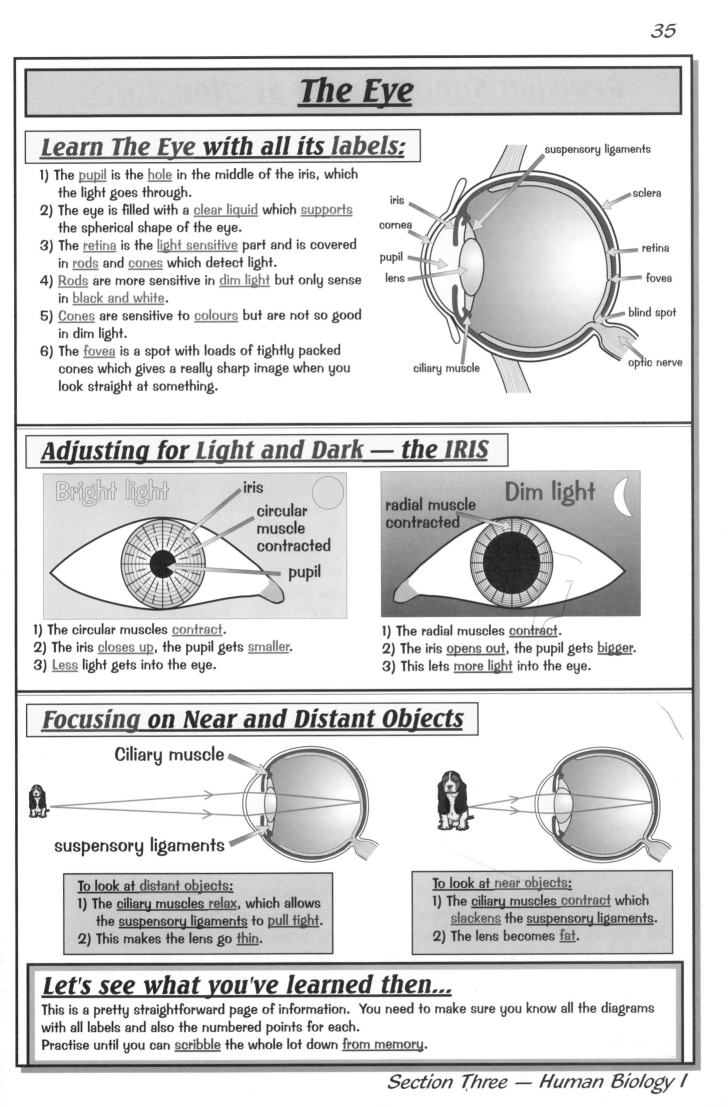

Adjusting for Light and Dark — the IRIS

Bright light

iris
circular muscle contracted
pupil

1) The circular muscles contract.
2) The iris closes up, the pupil gets smaller.
3) Less light gets into the eye.

Dim light

radial muscle contracted

1) The radial muscles contract.
2) The iris opens out, the pupil gets bigger.
3) This lets more light into the eye.

Focusing on Near and Distant Objects

Ciliary muscle

suspensory ligaments

To look at distant objects:
1) The ciliary muscles relax, which allows the suspensory ligaments to pull tight.
2) This makes the lens go thin.

To look at near objects:
1) The ciliary muscles contract which slackens the suspensory ligaments.
2) The lens becomes fat.

Let's see what you've learned then...

This is a pretty straightforward page of information. You need to make sure you know all the diagrams with all labels and also the numbered points for each.
Practise until you can scribble the whole lot down from memory.

Revision Summary for Section Three

Phew, there's a lot of stuff to learn in Section Three. And it's all that grisly "open heart surgery" type stuff too, with all those gory diagrams. Mind you, it's all fairly straightforward and factual — you know, nothing difficult to understand, just lots of facts to learn. And lots of gory diagrams. You know the big plan with these questions though. Keep practising till you can whizz them all off without a moment's hesitation on any of them. It's a nice trick if you can do it.

1) Sketch a diagram of the digestive system and put the ten labels on it.

2) Write down at least two details for each of the ten labelled parts.

3) Draw a diagram of a peristaltic squeeze and label the different types of tissue, with their use.

4) Sketch a villus, and say what it's for. Point out the three main features of villi.

5) Detail the three boring food tests: a) starch   b) protein   c) simple sugars.

6) What *exactly* do enzymes do in the digestive system?

7) List the three digestive enzymes, which foods they act on, and what they produce.

8) What *two* things does bile do? Where is it produced? Where does it enter the system?

9) What are the three "big" food molecules, and which kind of foods are each of them found in?

10) What small molecules are they each broken down into in the digestive system?

11) Sketch a diagram showing what then happens to the small molecules.

12) Draw a diagram of the human circulatory system: heart, lungs, arteries, veins, etc.

13) Explain why it is a *double* circulatory system, and describe the pressure and oxygen content of the blood in each bit. What are the big words for saying if the blood has oxygen in or not?

14) Sketch an artery, a capillary, and a vein, with labels, and explain the features of all three.

15) Draw a full diagram of the heart with all the labels.   Explain how the two halves differ.

16) How do ventricles and atria compare, and why? What are the valves for?

17) Describe briefly with diagrams the three stages of the pumping cycle for the heart.

18) Sketch a red blood cell and a white blood cell and give five details about each.

19) Sketch some blood plasma. List all the things that are carried in the plasma (around 10).

20) Sketch some platelets. What do they do all day?

21) Draw a diagram of the thorax, showing all the breathing equipment.

22) Describe what happens during breathing in and breathing out. Be sure to give all the details.

23) Where are alveoli found? How big are they and what are they for? Give four features.

24) Explain what happens to oxygen and carbon dioxide, both at alveoli and at body cells.

25) What is respiration? Give a proper definition.

26) What is the composition of inhaled and exhaled air? Give two comments on the difference.

27) What is "aerobic respiration"? Give the word and symbol equations for it.

28) What is "anaerobic respiration"? Give the word equation for what happens in our bodies.

29) Explain about fitness and the oxygen debt.

30) What is the word equation for fermentation? Name one product that's made using fermentation.

31) Draw a diagram showing the main parts of the nervous system.

32) List the five sense organs and say what kind of receptors each one has.

33) What are effectors? What two things constitute the central nervous system?

34) What are the three types of neurone? Draw a detailed diagram of a typical neurone.

35) Explain how a synapse works.

36) Describe how a reflex arc works and why it's a good thing.

37) Draw a full diagram of an eye with all labels and details.

38) Describe how the eye adjusts for light and dark, and to focus on near and distant objects.

Section Three — Human Biology I

Hormones

Hormones are Chemical Messengers sent in the Blood

1) Hormones are chemicals released directly into the <u>blood</u>.
2) They are carried in the blood to other parts of the body.
3) They are produced in various <u>glands</u> (endocrine glands) as shown on the diagram.
4) They travel all over the body but only affect <u>particular cells</u> in particular places.
5) They travel at "<u>the speed of blood</u>".
6) They have <u>long-lasting effects</u>.
7) They control things that need <u>constant adjustment</u>.

> **learn this definition:**
>
> Hormones ...
> are <u>chemical messengers</u>
> which <u>travel in the blood</u>
> to <u>activate target cells</u>.

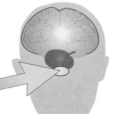

The Pituitary Gland

This produces many important hormones: <u>LH</u>, <u>FSH</u> and <u>ADH</u>.
These tend to <u>control</u> other glands, as a rule.

Adrenal Gland

Produces <u>adrenaline</u> which prepares the body with the well known <u>fight</u> or <u>flight</u> reaction:

> <u>Increased</u> *blood sugar, heart rate, breathing rate, and* <u>diversion</u> *of blood from skin to muscles.*

Pancreas

Produces <u>insulin</u> for the control of <u>blood sugar</u>
(If you're doing AQA it also produces <u>glucagon</u>).

Kidney

Ovaries — females only

Produce <u>oestrogen</u> which promotes all <u>female</u> secondary sexual characteristics during puberty:
1) <u>Extra hair</u> in places.
2) Changes in body <u>proportions</u>.
3) <u>Egg</u> production.

Testes — males only

Produce <u>testosterone</u> which promotes all <u>male</u> secondary sexual characteristics at puberty:
1) <u>Extra hair</u> in places.
2) Changes in body <u>proportions</u>.
3) <u>Sperm</u> production.

Hormones and Nerves do Similar Jobs, but there are Important Differences

Nerves:
1) Very <u>fast</u> message.
2) Act for a very <u>short time</u>.
3) Act on a very <u>precise area</u>.
4) <u>Immediate</u> reaction.

Hormones:
1) <u>Slower</u> message.
2) Act for a <u>long time</u>.
3) Act in a more <u>general</u> way.
4) <u>Longer-term</u> reaction.

Hormones — Easy peasy...

Well let's face it, there's not much to learn here is there? The diagram and all its labels are easy enough, and so's the comparison of nerves and hormones. The definition of hormones is worth learning word for word. The seven points at the top of the page are best done with the good old "mini-essay" method. <u>Learn it</u>, <u>cover the page</u> and <u>scribble</u>. Then <u>try again</u>.   And smile of course.

Hormones in the Menstrual Cycle

The Menstrual Cycle has Four Stages

Stage 1   Day 1 is when the bleeding starts. The uterus lining breaks down for about four days.

Stage 2   The lining of the womb builds up again, from day 4 to day 14, into a thick spongy layer of blood vessels ready to receive a fertilised egg.

Stage 3   An egg is developed and then released from the ovary at about day 14.

Stage 4   The wall is then maintained for about 14 days, until day 28.   If no fertilised egg has landed on the uterus wall by day 28 then the spongy lining starts to break down again and the whole cycle starts over. The diagram below illustrates this.

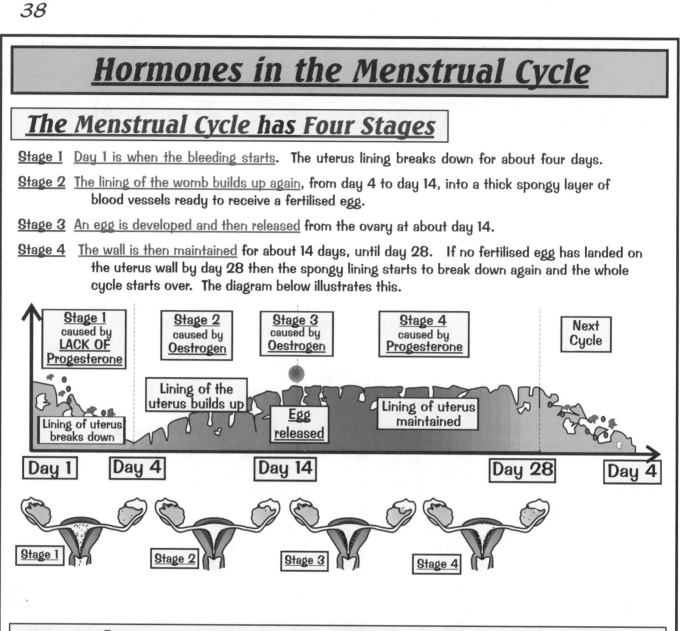

Female Hormones are Used to Control Babies

FSH is Used to Stimulate Egg Production in Fertility Treatment

1) A hormone called FSH can be taken by women to stimulate egg production in their ovaries.
2) In fact FSH (Follicle Stimulating Hormone) stimulates the ovaries to produce oestrogen which in turn stimulates the release of an egg.
3) But you do have to be careful with the dosage or you get too many eggs resulting in multiple births.

Oestrogen is Used to Stop Egg Production in "The PILL"

1) "The Pill", as it's cheerfully known, contains both progesterone and oestrogen.
2) It may seem kind of strange but even though oestrogen stimulates the release of eggs, if oestrogen is taken every day to keep the level of it permanently high, it inhibits the production of FSH and after a while egg production stops and stays stopped.

Female or otherwise, you've still gotta learn it...

This is the relatively simple stuff on the menstrual cycle and it's definitely well worth learning. Make sure you know what the four stages in the cycle are and which hormones are responsible for them, and also which hormones are used to control babies.   Learn and enjoy.

Hormones in the Menstrual Cycle

Oestrogen and Progesterone are The Two Main Hormones

These two hormones are produced in the <u>ovaries</u> and they control the main events of the cycle:

1) Oestrogen:	1) Causes the lining of the uterus to <u>thicken</u> and <u>grow</u>.
	2) Stimulates the <u>release of an egg</u> at day 14.

2) Progesterone:	1) <u>Maintains</u> the lining of the uterus.
	When the level of progesterone <u>falls</u>, the lining <u>breaks down</u>.

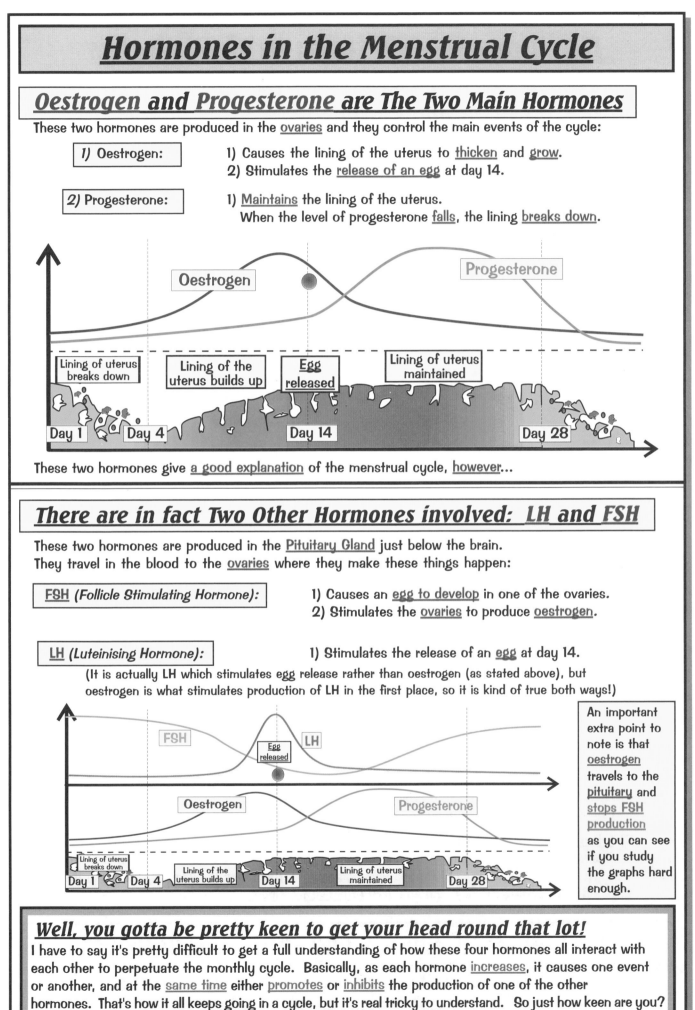

These two hormones give <u>a good explanation</u> of the menstrual cycle, <u>however...</u>

There are in fact Two Other Hormones involved: LH and FSH

These two hormones are produced in the <u>Pituitary Gland</u> just below the brain.
They travel in the blood to the <u>ovaries</u> where they make these things happen:

FSH (Follicle Stimulating Hormone):	1) Causes an <u>egg to develop</u> in one of the ovaries.
	2) Stimulates the <u>ovaries</u> to produce <u>oestrogen</u>.

LH (Luteinising Hormone):	1) Stimulates the release of an <u>egg</u> at day 14.

(It is actually LH which stimulates egg release rather than oestrogen (as stated above), but oestrogen is what stimulates production of LH in the first place, so it is kind of true both ways!)

An important extra point to note is that <u>oestrogen</u> travels to the <u>pituitary</u> and <u>stops FSH production</u> as you can see if you study the graphs hard enough.

Well, you gotta be pretty keen to get your head round that lot!

I have to say it's pretty difficult to get a full understanding of how these four hormones all interact with each other to perpetuate the monthly cycle. Basically, as each hormone <u>increases</u>, it causes one event or another, and at the <u>same time</u> either <u>promotes</u> or <u>inhibits</u> the production of one of the other hormones. That's how it all keeps going in a cycle, but it's real tricky to understand. So just how keen are you?

Hormones — Insulin and Diabetes

Insulin is a hormone which controls how much sugar there is in your blood. LEARN how it does it:

Insulin Controls Blood Sugar Levels

1) Eating carbohydrate foods puts a lot of glucose into the blood from the gut.
2) Normal metabolism of cells removes glucose from the blood.
3) Vigorous exercise removes much more glucose from the blood.
4) Obviously, to keep the level of blood glucose controlled there has to be a way to add or remove glucose from the blood. And this is it:

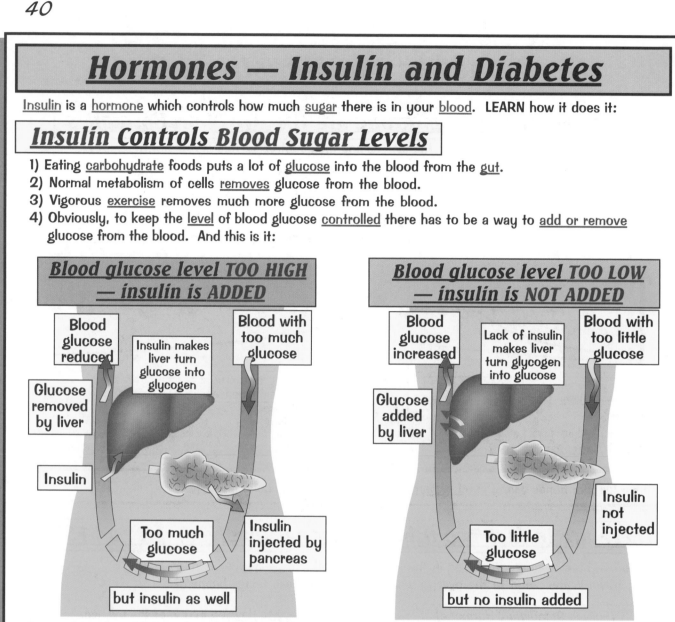

Blood glucose level TOO HIGH — insulin is ADDED

Blood glucose reduced

Insulin makes liver turn glucose into glycogen

Blood with too much glucose

Glucose removed by liver

Insulin

Too much glucose

Insulin injected by pancreas

but insulin as well

Blood glucose level TOO LOW — insulin is NOT ADDED

Blood glucose increased

Lack of insulin makes liver turn glycogen into glucose

Blood with too little glucose

Glucose added by liver

Too little glucose

Insulin not injected

but no insulin added

Remember, the addition of insulin reduces blood sugar level.
(For AQA syllabuses you also need to know that when the blood sugar is too low, another hormone called Glucagon is added instead of insulin. Glucagon makes the liver release glucose into the blood.)

Diabetes — the Pancreas Stops Making Enough Insulin

1) Diabetes is a disease in which the pancreas doesn't produce enough insulin.
2) The result is that a person's blood sugar can rise to a level that can kill them.
3) The problem can be controlled in two ways:

A) Avoiding foods rich in carbohydrate (which turns to glucose when digested).
It can also be helpful to take exercise after eating carbohydrates... i.e. trying to use up the extra glucose by doing physical activity, but this isn't usually very practical.

B) Injecting insulin into the blood before meals, (especially if high in carbohydrates).
This will make the liver remove the glucose from the blood as soon as it enters it from the gut, when the (carbohydrate-rich) food is being digested. This stops the level of glucose in the blood from getting too high and is a very effective treatment.

Learn all this stuff about blood sugar and diabetes...

This stuff on blood sugar and insulin can seem a bit confusing at first, but if you concentrate on learning those two diagrams, it'll all start to get a lot easier. Don't forget that only carbohydrate foods put the blood sugar levels up. Learn it all, then cover the page and scribble it all down.

Homeostasis

Homeostasis is a fancy word.

DON'T GET IT CONFUSED WITH HORMONES COZ THEY ARE COMPLETELY DIFFERENT THINGS... OK!

Homeostasis covers all the functions of your body which try to maintain a "constant internal environment".

Learn the definition:

HOMEOSTASIS — *the maintenance of a CONSTANT INTERNAL ENVIRONMENT*

There are six different bodily levels that need to be controlled:

1) REMOVAL OF CO_2
2) REMOVAL OF Urea } These two are wastes. They're constantly produced in the body and you just need to get rid of them.

3) Ion content
4) Water content
5) Sugar content
6) Temperature } These four are all "goodies" and we need them, but at just the right level — not too much and not too little.

Learn the Organs Involved in Homeostasis:

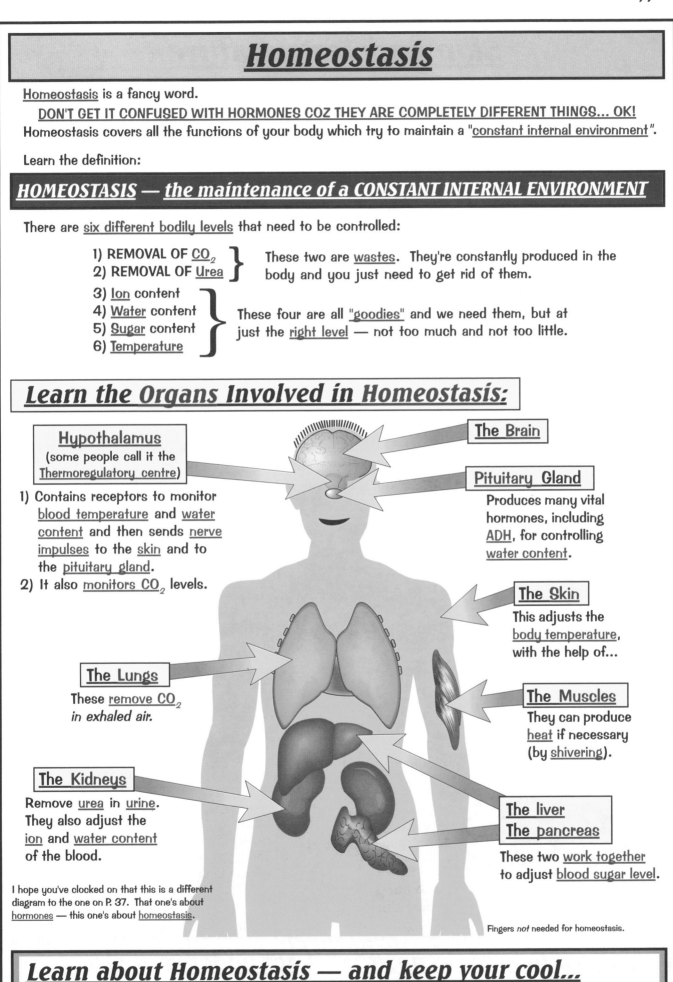

Hypothalamus
(some people call it the Thermoregulatory centre)

1) Contains receptors to monitor blood temperature and water content and then sends nerve impulses to the skin and to the pituitary gland.
2) It also monitors CO_2 levels.

The Brain

Pituitary Gland
Produces many vital hormones, including ADH, for controlling water content.

The Skin
This adjusts the body temperature, with the help of...

The Muscles
They can produce heat if necessary (by shivering).

The Lungs
These remove CO_2 in exhaled air.

The Kidneys
Remove urea in urine. They also adjust the ion and water content of the blood.

The liver The pancreas
These two work together to adjust blood sugar level.

I hope you've clocked on that this is a different diagram to the one on P. 37. That one's about hormones — this one's about homeostasis.

Fingers *not* needed for homeostasis.

Learn about Homeostasis — and keep your cool...

This is all a bit technical. Homeostasis is really quite a complicated business. It's just a good job it does it automatically or we'd all be in real trouble. You still gotta learn it for your Exam though. Scribble.

Skin and Temperature

Controlling Our Body Temperature

All enzymes work best at a certain temperature. The enzymes in the human body work best at about 37°C. To keep your enzymes at warm and toasty 37°C your body does these things:

When you're too cold your body shivers (increasing your metabolism) to produce heat.

When you're too hot you produce sweat which cools you down.

1) There is a thermoregulatory centre in the brain which acts as your own personal thermostat.

2) It contains receptors that are sensitive to the blood temperature in the brain.

3) The thermoregulatory (there's that long word again) centre also receives impulses from the skin.

4) These impulses provide information about skin temperature.

The Skin has Three Tricks for Altering Body Temperature

1) The thermoregulatory centre senses changes and sends nervous impulses to the skin.

2) The skin then has three tricks for controlling body temperature:

no sweat

hairs erect

blood supply shut off

When you're TOO COLD:
1) Hairs stand on end to keep you warm.
2) No sweat is produced.
3) The blood supply to the skin closes off.

Oil gland

Sweat Gland

hair erector muscle

capillary network

When you're TOO HOT:
1) Hairs lie flat.
2) Sweat is produced which evaporates to cool you down.
3) The blood supply to the skin opens up to release body heat.

So much to learn — don't let it get under your skin...

I can count about 12 important facts to learn on this page, plus a couple of suitably splendid diagrams. Learn the headings for each section, then cover the page and scribble out the details.

Kidneys

Kidneys basically act as filters to "clean the blood"

The <u>kidneys</u> perform <u>three main roles</u>:

> 1) <u>Removal of urea</u> from the blood.
> 2) <u>Adjustment of ions</u> in the blood.
> 3) <u>Adjustment of water content</u> of the blood.

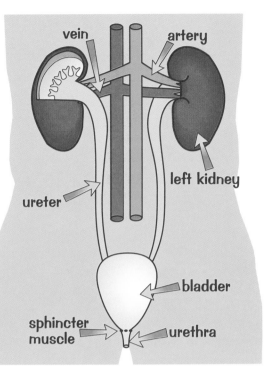

1) Removal of Urea

1) <u>Urea</u> is produced in the <u>liver</u>.

2) Proteins can't be *stored* by the body so <u>excess amino acids</u> are *broken down* by the liver into fats and carbohydrates.

3) The *waste product* is <u>urea</u> which is passed into the blood to be <u>filtered out</u> by the <u>kidneys</u>. Urea is also lost partly in <u>sweat</u>. Urea is <u>poisonous</u>.

2) Adjustment of Ion Content

1) <u>Ions</u>, such as sodium are taken into the body in <u>food</u>, and then absorbed into the blood.

2) Excess ions are <u>removed</u> by the kidneys. For example, a salty meal will contain far too much and the kidneys will <u>remove the excess</u> from the blood.

3) Some ions are also lost in <u>sweat</u> (which tastes salty, you'll have noticed).

4) But the important thing to remember is that the <u>balance</u> is always maintained by the <u>kidneys</u>.

3) Adjustment of Water Content

Water is *taken in* to the body as *food and drink* and is <u>lost</u> from the body in <u>three ways</u>:
> 1) in <u>urine</u> 2) in <u>sweat</u> 3) in <u>breath</u>

There's a need for the body to <u>constantly balance</u> the water coming in against the water going out. The amount lost in the *breath* is fairly *constant*, which means the <u>water balance</u> is between:
> 1) Liquids <u>consumed</u>
> 2) Amount <u>sweated out</u>
> 3) Amount <u>dumped by the kidneys</u> in the <u>urine</u>.

<u>On a cold day</u>, if you <u>don't sweat</u>, you'll produce <u>more urine</u> which will be <u>pale and dilute</u>.
<u>On a hot day</u>, you <u>sweat a lot</u>, your urine will be <u>dark-coloured</u>, <u>concentrated</u> and <u>little of it</u>. The water lost when it is hot has to be taken in as food and drink to restore the balance.

How Much Do You Know About Kidneys? — Let's See...

Phew. There's some stuff on this page isn't there. It's definitely a perfect candidate for the exciting mini-essay method. Learn the three headings, then <u>cover the page</u>, write them down, and then <u>scribble a mini-essay</u> for each one. Then look back and see what you missed. <u>Then try again</u>. And learn the diagram, until you can repeat that too.

Ultrafiltration and The Nephron

(Wasn't that a Star Trek episode?)

Nephrons are the Filtration Units in the Kidneys

1) Ultrafiltration:

1) A <u>high pressure</u> is built up which squeezes <u>water</u>, <u>urea</u>, <u>ions</u> and <u>glucose</u> out of the blood and into the <u>Bowman's capsule</u>.

2) However, <u>big molecules</u> like proteins are <u>not</u> squeezed out. They stay in the blood.

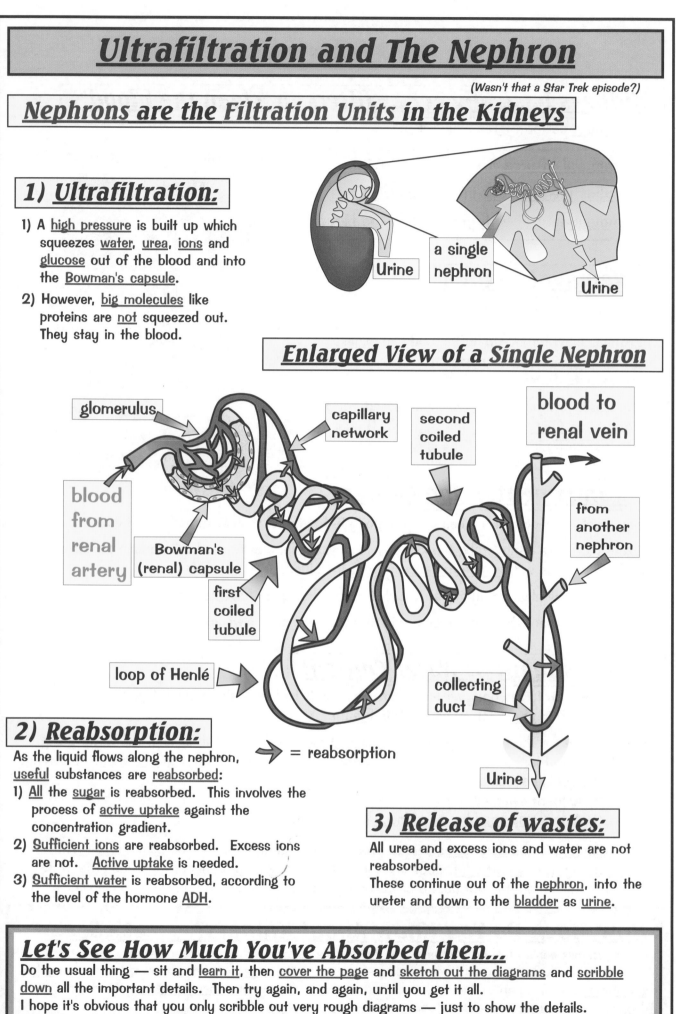

Urine

a single nephron

Urine

Enlarged View of a Single Nephron

glomerulus

capillary network

second coiled tubule

blood to renal vein

blood from renal artery

Bowman's (renal) capsule

first coiled tubule

from another nephron

loop of Henlé

2) Reabsorption:

As the liquid flows along the nephron, <u>useful</u> substances are <u>reabsorbed</u>:

1) <u>All</u> the <u>sugar</u> is reabsorbed. This involves the process of <u>active uptake</u> against the concentration gradient.

2) <u>Sufficient ions</u> are reabsorbed. Excess ions are not. <u>Active uptake</u> is needed.

3) <u>Sufficient water</u> is reabsorbed, according to the level of the hormone <u>ADH</u>.

⟹ = reabsorption

collecting duct

Urine

3) Release of wastes:

All urea and excess ions and water are not reabsorbed.

These continue out of the <u>nephron</u>, into the ureter and down to the <u>bladder</u> as <u>urine</u>.

Let's See How Much You've Absorbed then...

Do the usual thing — sit and <u>learn it</u>, then <u>cover the page</u> and <u>sketch out the diagrams</u> and <u>scribble down</u> all the important details. Then try again, and again, until you get it all.

I hope it's obvious that you only scribble out very rough diagrams — just to show the details.

ADH — Anti Diuretic Hormone

The <u>hypothalamus</u> in the brain <u>monitors the water content of the blood</u> and instructs the <u>pituitary gland</u> to release <u>ADH</u> into the blood <u>accordingly</u>, as shown below:

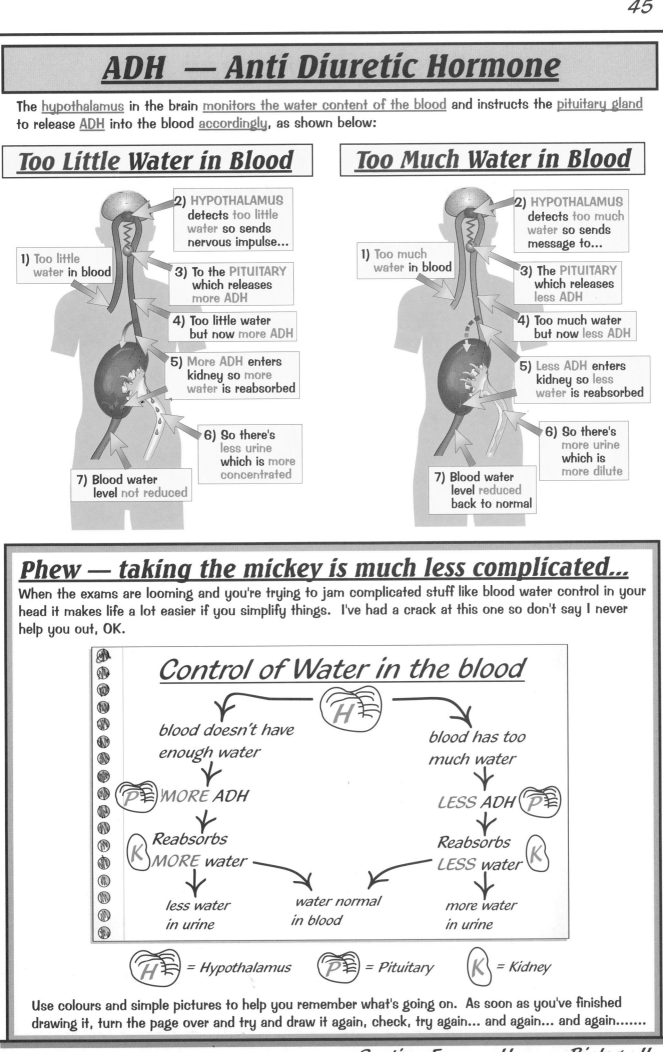

Too Little Water in Blood

1) Too little water in blood

2) HYPOTHALAMUS detects too little water so sends nervous impulse...

3) To the PITUITARY which releases more ADH

4) Too little water but now more ADH

5) More ADH enters kidney so more water is reabsorbed

6) So there's less urine which is more concentrated

7) Blood water level not reduced

Too Much Water in Blood

1) Too much water in blood

2) HYPOTHALAMUS detects too much water so sends message to...

3) The PITUITARY which releases less ADH

4) Too much water but now less ADH

5) Less ADH enters kidney so less water is reabsorbed

6) So there's more urine which is more dilute

7) Blood water level reduced back to normal

Phew — taking the mickey is much less complicated...

When the exams are looming and you're trying to jam complicated stuff like blood water control in your head it makes life a lot easier if you simplify things. I've had a crack at this one so don't say I never help you out, OK.

Control of Water in the blood

blood doesn't have enough water

blood has too much water

MORE ADH

LESS ADH

Reabsorbs MORE water

Reabsorbs LESS water

less water in urine

water normal in blood

more water in urine

H = Hypothalamus   P = Pituitary   K = Kidney

Use colours and simple pictures to help you remember what's going on. As soon as you've finished drawing it, turn the page over and try and draw it again, check, try again... and again... and again.......

Disease in Humans

There are two types of Micro-organism: Bacteria and Viruses

Micro-organisms are organisms which get inside you and make you feel ill. There are two main types:

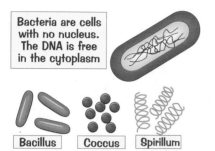

Bacteria are cells with no nucleus. The DNA is free in the cytoplasm

Bacillus   Coccus   Spirillum

Bacteria are Very Small Living Cells

1) These are <u>very small cells</u>, (about 1/100th the size of your body cells), which reproduce rapidly inside your body.

2) They make you feel ill by doing <u>two</u> things:
       a) <u>damaging</u> your <u>cells</u>   b) producing <u>toxins</u>.

3) Don't forget that some bacteria are <u>useful</u> if they're in the <u>right place</u>, like in your digestive system.

Viruses are not cells — they're much smaller

1) These are <u>not</u> cells. They are very very small, about 1/100th the size of a bacterium.

2) They are no more than a <u>coat</u> of <u>protein</u> around a <u>DNA strand</u>.

3) They make you feel ill by damaging your cells.

4) They <u>replicate themselves</u> by invading the nucleus of a cell and using the <u>DNA</u> it contains to produce many <u>copies</u> of themselves.

5) The cell then <u>bursts</u>, releasing all the new viruses.

6) In this way they can reproduce <u>very quickly</u>.

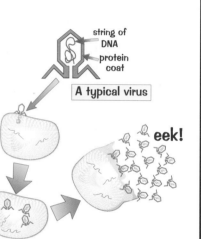

string of DNA

protein coat

A typical virus

eek!

Three ways our bodies defend against micro-organisms

Micro-organisms can enter our bodies in different ways, but we do have some <u>defences</u>.

1) The Skin and Eyes

<u>Undamaged skin</u> is a very effective barrier against micro-organisms. If it gets damaged, the blood <u>clots</u> quickly to <u>seal cuts</u> and keep the micro-organisms out.
<u>Eyes</u> produce a chemical which <u>kills bacteria</u> on the surface of the eye.

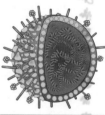

A horrid Flu Virus

2) The Digestive System

<u>Contaminated food</u> and <u>dirty water</u> allow micro-organisms to enter your body. The stomach produces strong <u>hydrochloric acid</u> which <u>kills</u> most micro-organisms which enter that way.

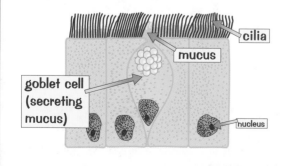

cilia

mucus

goblet cell (secreting mucus)

nucleus

3) The Respiratory System

The whole <u>respiratory tract</u> (nasal passage, trachea and lungs) is lined with <u>mucus</u> and <u>cilia</u> which catch <u>dust</u> and <u>bacteria</u> before they reach the lungs.

Fighting Disease

Once micro-organisms have entered our bodies they will <u>reproduce rapidly</u> unless they are destroyed. Your '<u>immune system</u>' does just that, and <u>white blood cells</u> are the most important part of it.

Your Immune System: White blood cells

They travel around in your blood and crawl into every part of you, constantly <u>patrolling</u> for micro-organisms. When they come across an invading micro-organism they have <u>three lines of attack</u>:

1) Consuming Them

White blood cells can <u>engulf</u> foreign cells and <u>digest</u> them.

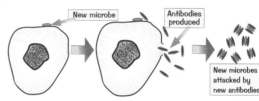

microbes

White Blood Cell

2) Producing Antibodies

When your white blood cells come across a <u>foreign cell</u> they will start to produce proteins called <u>antibodies</u> to kill the new invading cells. The antibodies are then produced <u>rapidly</u> and flow all round the body to kill all <u>similar</u> bacteria or viruses.

New microbe

Antibodies produced

New microbes attacked by new antibodies

3) Producing Antitoxins

<u>Antitoxins</u> counter the effect of any <u>poisons</u> (toxins) produced by the <u>invading bacteria</u>.

Immunisation — Getting antibodies ready for attack

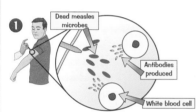

Dead measles microbes

Antibodies produced

White blood cell

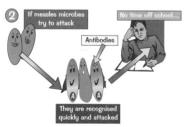

If measles microbes try to attack

Antibodies

No time off school...

They are recognised quickly and attacked

1) Once your white cells have produced antibodies to tackle a new strain of bacteria or virus you are said to have developed "<u>natural immunity</u>" to it.

2) This means if the <u>same micro-organisms</u> attack again they'll be killed by the <u>antibodies</u> you already have for them, and you <u>won't get ill</u>.

3) The trouble is when a <u>new</u> micro-organism appears, it takes your white blood cells a few days to produce the antibodies to deal with them and in that time you can get <u>very ill</u>.

4) There are plenty of diseases which can make you very ill indeed (e.g. polio, tetanus, measles) and only <u>immunisation</u> stops you getting them.

5) Immunisation involves injecting <u>dead</u> micro-organisms into you. This causes your body to produce <u>antibodies</u> to attack them, even though they're dead. They can do no <u>harm</u> to you because they're dead.

6) If <u>live</u> micro-organisms of the same type appeared after that, they'd be <u>killed immediately</u> by the antibodies which you have already developed against them. Cool.

Antibiotics kill Bacteria but NOT Viruses

1) <u>Antibiotics</u> are drugs that kill <u>bacteria</u> without killing your own body cells.

2) They are very useful for clearing up infections that your body is having <u>trouble</u> with.

3) However they don't kill <u>viruses</u>.
<u>Flu and colds</u> are caused by <u>viruses</u> and basically, you're on your own, pal.

4) There are <u>no drugs</u> to kill <u>viruses</u> and you just have to <u>wait</u> for your body to deal with it and <u>suffer</u> in the meantime.

5) Still, it's better than being bitten by a rat flea.

A horrid Flu Virus

An even more horrid Rat Flea

It's Grisly Stuff, but worth learning just the same...

Two pages this time, and definitely 'mini-essay' material. There are four main sections, with several subsections. Do a <u>mini-essay</u> on each subsection and then <u>check</u> what you forgot.

Drugs

1) Drugs are substances which alter the way the body works. Some drugs are useful of course, for example antibiotics such as penicillin. However there are many drugs which are <u>dangerous</u> if misused, and many of them are <u>addictive</u> or "habit-forming".

2) The loss of control and judgement caused by many drugs can easily lead to <u>death</u> from various other causes, e.g. getting HIV or hepatitis from used needles, choking on vomit... Horrible, horrible things.

There are two types of Addiction — Chemical and Psychological

1) There's a difference between true <u>chemical addiction</u> and <u>psychological addiction</u>.

2) In <u>chemical addiction</u> the body becomes adjusted to the constant presence of the drug in the system. If the drug is withdrawn, there are various <u>unpleasant physical withdrawal symptoms</u>: fevers, hallucinations, nausea, and the shakes.

3) <u>Psychological addiction</u> is where the person "feels the need" to keep taking the drug.

Stimulants

1) <u>Stimulants</u> tend to make the nervous system generally more alert and "awake".

2) Caffeine is a mild stimulant found in tea and coffee. It's pretty harmless. Few lives are wrecked by obsessive tea-drinking.

3) However, amphetamine and methedrine are also stimulants.

4) Strong stimulants like these produce a feeling of boundless energy, but the person experiences <u>serious depression</u> if they stop taking it, so an unhealthy <u>dependence</u> develops all too easily. Continued use can lead to hallucinations and <u>changes in personality</u>.

<u>Depressants</u> tend to slow down the responses of the nervous system, causing <u>slow reactions</u> and poor judgement of speed, distances, etc. See "Alcohol" on the next page.

Pain Killers — Aspirin, Heroin and Morphine

1) Heroin is a <u>particularly nasty</u> drug causing a serious <u>deterioration</u> in personality and as the addiction grows the person's whole life <u>degenerates</u> into a <u>desperate struggle</u> to obtain money for their daily heroin requirement, often resulting in a <u>sad life of crime</u> to pay for it.

2) Morphine is also highly <u>addictive</u>.

3) Aspirin is a useful painkiller for many minor illnesses, but its overuse has <u>harmful effects</u>.

Solvents

1) Solvents are found in a variety of "household" items e.g. glues, paints etc.

2) They are <u>dangerous</u> and have many <u>damaging effects</u> on your body and personality.

3) They cause hallucinations and adversely affect personality and behaviour.

4) They cause <u>damage</u> to the <u>lungs</u>, <u>brain</u>, <u>liver</u> and <u>kidney</u>.

Learn about these drugs and then forget them...

Anyone with half a brain avoids these drugs like they do <u>rat fleas</u>.
Enjoy your life, instead of being a sucker.

Drugs

1) Alcohol and tobacco are the two main (non-medical) drugs which are legal in this country.
2) But don't be fooled. They can do you a lot of harm just like the other drugs can.

Alcohol

1) The main effect of alcohol is to reduce the activity of the nervous system. The positive aspect of this is that it makes us feel less inhibited, and there's no doubt that alcohol in moderation helps people to socialise and relax with each other.
2) However, if you let alcohol take over, it can wreck your life. And it does. It wrecks a lot of people's lives. You've got to control it.
3) Once alcohol starts to take over someone's life there are many harmful effects:
   a) Alcohol is basically poisonous. Too much drinking will cause severe damage to the liver and the brain leading to liver disease and a noticeable drop in brain function.
   b) Too much alcohol impairs judgement which can cause accidents, and it can also severely affect the person's work and home life.
   c) Serious dependency on alcohol will eventually lead to loss of job, loss of income and the start of a severe downward spiral.

Smoking Tobacco

Smoking is no good to anyone except the cigarette companies.
And once you've started smoking there's no going back. It's a one way trip pal.

And you'll notice that smokers are no happier than non-smokers, even when they're smoking. What may start off as something "different" to do, rapidly becomes something they have to do, just to feel OK. But non-smokers feel just as OK without spending £20 or more each week and wrecking their health into the bargain.

And why do people start smoking? To look the part, that's why. They have an image in their head of how they want to appear and smoking seems the perfect fashion accessory.

Well just remember, it's a one way trip. You might think it makes you look cool at 16, but will it still seem the perfect fashion accessory when you're 20 with a new group of friends who don't smoke? Nope. Too late. You're stuck with it.

And by the time you're 60 it'll have cost you over £40,000. Enough to buy a Ferrari or a new house. That's quite an expensive fashion accessory.
Smoking? Cool? Oh yeah — it's about as cool as cool can be, I'd say.

DEATH TUBES

WARNING
SMOKING CAUSES:
WRINKLED AND THIN SKIN
HAIR LOSS
STAINED TEETH AND FINGERS
BREATHLESSNESS
BAD BREATH
GUM DISEASE
EMPHYSEMA
BRONCHITIS
LUNG CANCER
HEART DISEASE

Oh and by the way...

Tobacco smoke does this inside your body:
1) It coats the inside of your lungs with tar so they become hideously inefficient.
2) It covers the cilia in tar preventing them from getting bacteria out of your lungs.
3) It causes disease of the heart and blood vessels, leading to heart attacks and strokes.
4) It causes lung cancer. Out of every ten lung cancer patients, nine of them smoke.

5) It causes severe loss of lung function leading to diseases like emphysema and bronchitis, in which the inside of the lungs is basically wrecked. People with severe bronchitis can't manage even a brisk walk, because their lungs can't get enough oxygen into the blood. It eventually kills over 20,000 people in Britain every year.
6) Carbon monoxide in tobacco smoke stops haemoglobin carrying as much oxygen. In pregnant women this deprives the fetus of oxygen leading to a small baby at birth. In short, "smoking chokes your baby".
7) But this is the best bit. The effect of the nicotine is negligible — other than to make you addicted to it. It doesn't make you high — just dependent. Great. Fantastic.

Smoking stains teeth yellow.
Brushing doesn't really get rid of it.

Learn the Numbered Points for your Exam...

It's the disease aspects they concentrate on most in the Exams. Learn the rest for a nice life.

Revision Summary for Section Four

Section Four's got all sorts of grisly bits and bobs in it. And some of it can be really quite hard to understand too. But it's all worth points in the Exam, and what do points mean? Prizes!
These questions are designed to test what you know. They're pretty tough I grant you, but they really are the best way of revising. Keep trying these questions any time you feel like it, and for any you can't do, look back in Section Four and learn the answer to it for next time.

1) Draw a diagram of the body and label the five places where hormones are produced.
   Give details of what each hormones does.
2) Give the proper definition of hormones.
3) Give four details to compare nerves with hormones.
4) Explain what happens with insulin when the blood sugar is too high and when it is too low.
5) Draw diagrams to illustrate exactly what goes on in both cases.
6) What happens in diabetes? What are the two forms of treatment? How do they compare?
7) Give brief details of the four stages in the female menstrual cycle.
8) Sketch the diagram showing the state of the uterus lining at each stage.
9) Give full details of which hormones are used: a) to promote fertility   b) in "The Pill".
10) What are the two main hormones involved in the female menstrual cycle?
11) Sketch the diagram showing the uterus lining and the levels of both hormones over the 28 days.
12) What are the other two hormones involved and where do they originate?
      Draw graphs showing the level of these other two hormones and explain what they both do.
13) What are the two types of micro-organism? How big are they compared to a human cell?
14) How exactly do bacteria make you feel ill? Sketch three common bacteria.
15) What do viruses do inside you to reproduce? Illustrate with sketches.
16) What are the five ways that micro-organisms can enter our bodies?
17) Give details of the defences we have against these five methods of entry.
18) What is meant by your "immune system"? What is the most important part of it?
19) List the three ways that white blood cells deal with invading micro-organisms.
20) Give full details of the process of immunisation. How does it work?
21) What are antibiotics? What will they work on and what will they not work on?
22) What are the two types of addiction to drugs?
23) List the three different types of "drug" with examples of each. List the dangers of each type.
24) Explain the dangers of drinking alcohol. Explain why smoking is just *so cool — not.*
25) List in detail all six major health problems that result from smoking.
26) What is the proper definition for homeostasis? What are the six bodily levels involved?
27) Draw a diagram of the body showing the eight organs involved in homeostasis.
28) Say exactly what each of these organs does to help.
29) What are the three main things that the skin does for you?
30) What temperature do our bodily enzymes like?
31) Which organ detects body temperature? How does it tell the skin about it?
32) Draw diagrams showing the three things the skin does when we're a) too hot b) too cold.
33) What is the basic function of the kidneys? What *three* particular things do they deal with?
34) Explain in detail exactly what the kidney does in relation to each of these three things.
35) Sketch a kidney to show where a nephron is and then roughly draw an enlarged nephron.
36) Label the main parts of it and describe the *three main processes* and where they all happen.
37) What is ADH and where is it produced?
38) Draw diagrams to explain how ADH is involved in regulating the water content of the blood.

Variation in Plants and Animals

1) Young plants and animals obviously <u>resemble</u> their <u>parents</u>. In other words they show <u>similar</u> <u>characteristics</u> such as jagged leaves or perfect eyebrows.

2) However young animals and plants can also <u>differ</u> from their parents and each other.

3) These similarities and differences lead to <u>variation</u> within the same species.

4) The word "<u>variation</u>" sounds far too fancy for its own good. All it means is how animals or plants of the same species <u>look</u> or <u>behave</u> slightly different from each other. You know, a bit <u>taller</u> or a bit <u>fatter</u> or a bit more <u>scary-to-look-at</u> etc.

There are <u>two</u> causes of variation: <u>Genetic Variation</u> and <u>Environmental Variation</u>.

Read on, and learn...

1) Genetic variation

You'll know this already.

1) <u>All animals</u> (including humans) are bound to be slightly different from each other because their <u>genes</u> are slightly different.

2) Genes are the code inside all your cells which determine how your body turns out. We all end up with a slightly different set of genes.

3) The <u>exceptions</u> to that rule are <u>identical twins</u>, because their genes are <u>exactly the same</u>.

But even identical twins are never <u>completely identical</u> — and that's because of the other factor:

2) Environmental Variation is shown up by Identical Twins

If you're not sure what "<u>environment</u>" means, think of it as "<u>upbringing</u>" instead — it's pretty much the same thing — how and where you were "brought up".

Since we know the <u>twins' genes</u> are <u>identical</u>, any differences between them <u>must</u> be caused by slight differences <u>in their environment</u> throughout their lives.

<u>Twins</u> give us a fairly good idea of how important the <u>two factors</u> (genes and environment) are, compared to each other, at least for animals — plants always show much <u>greater variation</u> due to differences in their environment than animals do, as explained below.

Environmental Variation in Plants is much Greater

Plants are strongly affected by:
1) <u>Temperature</u>
2) <u>Sunlight</u>
3) <u>Moisture level</u>
4) <u>Soil composition</u>

For example, plants may grow <u>twice as big</u> or <u>twice as fast</u> due to <u>fairly modest</u> changes in environment such as the amount of <u>sunlight</u> or <u>rainfall</u> they're getting, or how <u>warm</u> it is or what the <u>soil</u> is like.

A cat, on the other hand, born and bred in the North of Scotland, could be sent out to live in equatorial Africa and would show no significant changes — it would look the same, eat the same, and it would probably still puke up everywhere.

Variation in Plants and Animals

Environmental Variation in Animals

Stubborn cats notwithstanding...

In Exams they do like questions on the effects of <u>environment</u> on animals.

Typically, they'll ask you <u>which features</u> of a human or a pet <u>might be affected</u> by their environment (i.e. the way they were "brought up").

In fact, <u>almost every single aspect</u> of a human (or animal) will be affected by <u>upbringing</u> in some way, however small, and in fact it's considerably easier to list the very few factors that <u>aren't</u> affected by environment and these are they:

4 Animal Characteristics NOT affected at all by Environment:

1) <u>Eye colour</u>.

2) <u>Hair colour</u> in most animals (but not humans where vanity plays a big part).

3) <u>Inherited diseases</u> like haemophilia, cystic fibrosis, etc.

4) <u>Blood group</u>.

And that's about it! So <u>learn those four</u> in case they ask you.

Combinations of Genetic and Environmental Variation

<u>Everything else</u> is determined by <u>a mixture</u> of <u>genetic</u> and <u>environmental</u> factors:
<u>Body weight</u>, <u>height</u>, <u>skin colour</u>, <u>condition of teeth</u>, <u>academic or athletic prowess</u>, etc. etc.

The <u>tricky</u> bit is working out just <u>how significant</u> environmental factors are for all these other features.

For example...

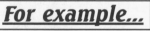

...imagine you got mixed up with another baby at the hospital and had grown up in a <u>totally different household</u> from your own. How different would you be now? It's not at all easy to tell how much of your <u>physique</u> and (more importantly) your <u>personality</u> are due to <u>genes</u> and how much to <u>upbringing</u> (<u>environment</u>). It's a big social issue, so it is.

Francis Galton — Is Intelligence Inherited

A History Lesson in Biology — <u>LEARN IT</u> AND TRY NOT TO WET YOURSELF WITH EXCITEMENT.

Francis Galton was a geezer who lived from 1822 to 1911. Through lots and lots of tests he reckoned that intelligence was determined by genetics although he did say that motivation affected results.
In normal-speak: "people get their brains from mum or dad, but some don't use them". Then he went off on one, saying that only brainy folk should marry brainy folk to increase the amount of brainy folk.

Nowadays the view is that genetics determines what your maximum intelligence could be...
But and it's a big <u>BUT</u>, nobody reaches their maximum intelligence. This means that <u>environmental</u> factors (like education) play a big role in how close your level of intelligence is to your maximum. Phew!

Don't let Everything get to you — just learn the facts...

There are seven sections on these two pages. After you think you've learnt it all, <u>cover the pages</u> and do a "<u>mini-essay</u>" on each of the seven sections. Then <u>check back</u> and see what important points you missed.

The Human Genome Project

It may sound like an investigation into ornamental garden pixies, but it's actually one of the <u>most exciting</u> things to happen in science for blummin ages. Some people have called it "more exciting than the first moon landing", or "the search for the <u>Holy Grail of science</u>". Maybe they should get out more.

Mapping the 30,000 Human Genes

The big idea was to find out what <u>every</u> single human gene did. Human DNA is made up of <u>3 billion</u> base pairs which make 30 000 genes curled up to form 23 chromosomes. Well now they've finished it.

> If you get an exam question about this stuff they'll ask you about what's good about it, what's bad about it or what's good and bad about it.

Here are the good bits and the bad bits — <u>learn</u> them and churn them out in the exam:

The Good Stuff — it can prevent a lot of suffering

1) <u>Predict and Prevent diseases</u>
   Doctors would know that someone has genes which increase their chances of getting a disease. They could give them regular checks to catch and treat it early, and advise on the best diet and lifestyle to avoid it. Better still, cures could be found for diseases such as Cystic Fibrosis and Sickle Cell Anaemia.

2) <u>Develop new and better medicines</u>
   Knowing exactly what causes a disease makes it easier to find medicines to target it and make medicines that are designed to work best for individuals.

3) <u>Accurate diagnoses</u>
   Some diseases are hard to test for, (eg you can only tell for sure if someone has Alzheimer's after they die) but now we know the genetic cause, accurate testing will be a lot easier. It's a heck of a lot easier treating something if you know what it is.

The Bad Stuff — It's a Scary World When You're not Perfect

It's easy to see how knowing more about the human body can do good, but the same knowledge may be a nightmare. Here are <u>four</u> big baddies that might be lurking in the future:

1) <u>Stress</u>
   WHAT MIGHT HAPPEN: *Someone will know from an early age that they're susceptible to a nasty brain disease. They may never get it, but they'll still panic every time they get a headache.*

2) <u>Gene-ism</u>
   WHAT MIGHT HAPPEN: *Everyone's genetic code becomes common knowledge and people with genetic problems are looked down on by the "genetically healthy". People with genetic problems find it harder to have relationships and are under pressure not to have children.*

3) <u>Discrimination by employers and insurers</u>
   WHAT MIGHT HAPPEN: *Life insurance may be impossible to get or blummin expensive if you have any genetic possibility of disease. Work will be much harder to get once all the application forms have a genetic health section.*

4) <u>Designer Babies</u>
   WHAT MIGHT HAPPEN: *Doctors can control exactly what genes are passed on to a baby. People don't want their baby to have genetic diseases, or be too aggressive, or be thick, or have to wear glasses, or have big ears.... and so on and so on. Everyone has to make their babies more and more "perfect" or they won't fit in with all the other disease-free, intelligent, models that are wandering around.*

DNA lipstick is part of my Genetic make-up...

If you still can't get it in yer head how this genome stuff could be bad news watch the film "Gattaca". The name is made up of the first letters of each of the 4 base pairs (Guanine, Adenine, Thymin, Cytosine). Cool.

Genetics: Too Many Fancy Words

When it comes to big fancy words then Biology is the subject where it's all happening.
And genetics is the topic that really walks away with all the prizes.
It seems hard to believe that so many exceptionally cumbersome, excessively complicated and virtually unintelligible words can conceivably be necessary, or indeed be particularly desirable...

Here's a summary of all the fancy words used in genetics with an explanation of what they actually mean. It really does make a big difference if you learn these first. It's very difficult to understand anything in genetics if you don't actually know what half the words mean.

DNA — is the molecule which contains genes. It's shaped like a double helix (a spiral).

Chromosomes — are those funny X-shaped things that are found in the cell nucleus. The arms are made up of very long coils of DNA, so chromosomes also contain genes.

Gene — is a section of DNA molecule. It's also part of the arm of a chromosome.

Allele — is a gene too. When you have two different versions of the same gene you have to call them alleles instead of genes. (It is more sensible than it sounds.)

Dominant — this refers to an allele or gene. The dominant allele is the one which will determine the characteristic which appears. It dominates the recessive allele on the other chromosome.

Recessive — is the allele which does not usually affect how the organism turns out because it's dominated by the dominant allele (fairly obviously).

Homozygous — is an individual with two alleles the same for that particular gene, e.g. HH or hh.

Heterozygous — is an individual with two alleles different for that particular gene, e.g. Hh.

Genotype — is simply a description of the genes you have, e.g. Mm or RR, that type of thing.

Phenotype — is the description of your physical attributes due to the genes in question i.e. your phenotype describes the physical result (e.g. "Bald") of your genotype, (e.g. "bb").

Mitosis — is the process of cell division where one cell splits into two identical cells.

Meiosis — is the other process of cell division which creates sperm or egg cells. Meiosis only happens in the ovaries or the testes.

Diploid — is the description of cells which have all 46 chromosomes i.e. BOTH sets of 23.

Haploid — is the description of cells which only have half the chromosomes, i.e. 23.

Gamete — is either a sperm cell or an egg cell.
All gametes are haploid — they only have 23 chromosomes.

Zygote — is the delightful name given to each newly-formed human life, just after the (equally delightfully-named) gametes fuse together at fertilisation.

You'd think they could have come up with some slightly prettier names, as would befit this most awesome and wonderful moment, really. Your whole life, that great voyage of discovery and wonder, of emotion and reason, of conscience and consciousness, begins with that fateful and magical moment when...
...''two GAMETES fuse to form a ZYGOTE''...   *Ahh, what poetry...*

Too many fancy words, but you still gotta learn 'em...

Practise by covering up the right hand side of the page and scribbling down a description for each word. That's nice and easy. Just keep looking back and practising till you can do them all.

Genes, Chromosomes and DNA

If you're going to get anywhere with this topic you definitely need to learn these confusing words and exactly what they mean. You have to make sure you know exactly what DNA is, what and where chromosomes are, and what and where a gene is. If you don't get that sorted out first, then anything else you read about them won't make a lot of sense to you — will it.

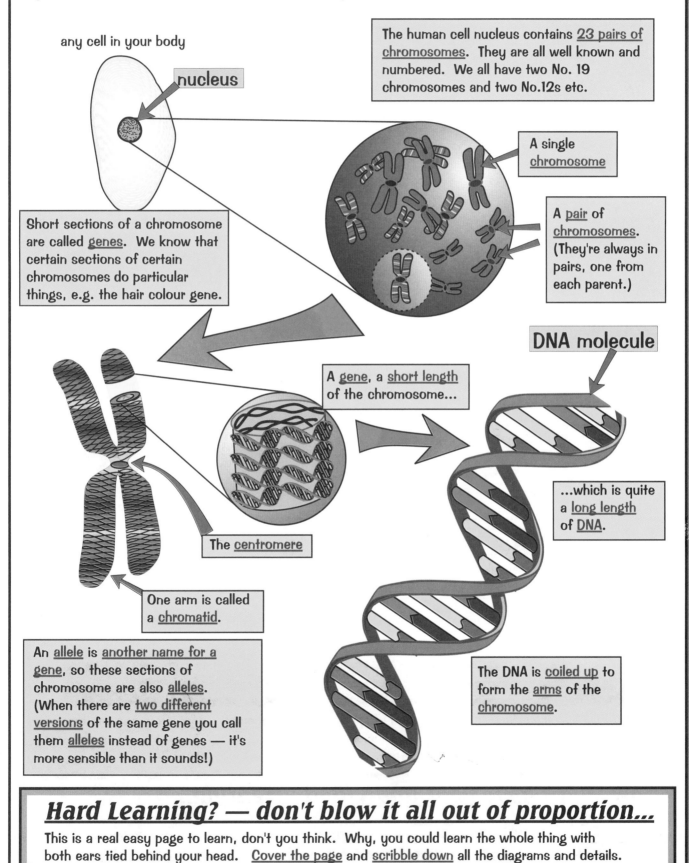

any cell in your body

nucleus

The human cell nucleus contains 23 pairs of chromosomes. They are all well known and numbered. We all have two No. 19 chromosomes and two No.12s etc.

A single chromosome

A pair of chromosomes. (They're always in pairs, one from each parent.)

Short sections of a chromosome are called genes. We know that certain sections of certain chromosomes do particular things, e.g. the hair colour gene.

DNA molecule

A gene, a short length of the chromosome...

...which is quite a long length of DNA.

The centromere

One arm is called a chromatid.

The DNA is coiled up to form the arms of the chromosome.

An allele is another name for a gene, so these sections of chromosome are also alleles. (When there are two different versions of the same gene you call them alleles instead of genes — it's more sensible than it sounds!)

Hard Learning? — don't blow it all out of proportion...

This is a real easy page to learn, don't you think. Why, you could learn the whole thing with both ears tied behind your head. Cover the page and scribble down all the diagrams and details.

Ordinary Cell Division: Mitosis

"Mitosis is when a cell reproduces itself by splitting to form two identical offspring."

The really riveting part of the whole process is how the chromosomes split inside the cell. Learn and enjoy...

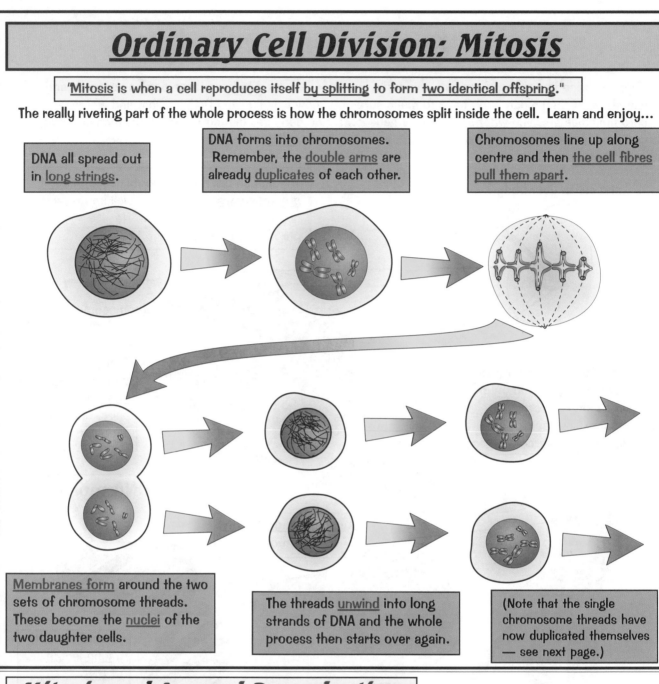

DNA all spread out in long strings.

DNA forms into chromosomes. Remember, the double arms are already duplicates of each other.

Chromosomes line up along centre and then the cell fibres pull them apart.

Membranes form around the two sets of chromosome threads. These become the nuclei of the two daughter cells.

The threads unwind into long strands of DNA and the whole process then starts over again.

(Note that the single chromosome threads have now duplicated themselves — see next page.)

Mitosis and Asexual Reproduction

Mitosis produces new cells identical to the original cell.

This is how all plants and animals grow and replace dead or damaged cells.

Their cells divide and multiply by the process of mitosis. However some organisms also reproduce using mitosis, bacteria being a good example. This is known as asexual reproduction. Here's a definition of it, for you to learn:

> In asexual reproduction there is only one parent, and the offspring therefore have exactly the same genes as the parent (i.e. they're clones — see P. 74).

This is because all the cells in both parent and offspring were produced by mitosis from one another, so they must all have identical genes in their cell nuclei.

Some plants reproduce asexually, e.g. potatoes, strawberries and daffodils (see P. 74).

Now that I have your undivided attention...

You need to learn the definition of mitosis and the sequence of diagrams, and also the definition of asexual reproduction. Now cover the page and scribble down the two definitions and sketch out the sequence of diagrams — don't waste time with neatness — just find out if you've learnt it all yet.

DNA Replication in Mitosis

Genes are Chemical Instructions

1) A gene is a length of DNA.
2) DNA is a long list of instructions on how to put the organism together and make it work.
3) Each separate gene is a separate chemical instruction to a particular type of cell.
4) Cells make proteins by stringing amino acids together in a particular order.
5) There are only about 20 different amino acids, but they make up thousands of different proteins.
6) Genes simply tell cells in what order to put the amino acids together.
7) That determines what proteins the cell produces, e.g. haemoglobin, or keratin, etc.
8) That in turn determines what type of cell it is, e.g. red blood cell, skin cell, etc.

DNA Replicates Itself to form Chromosomes

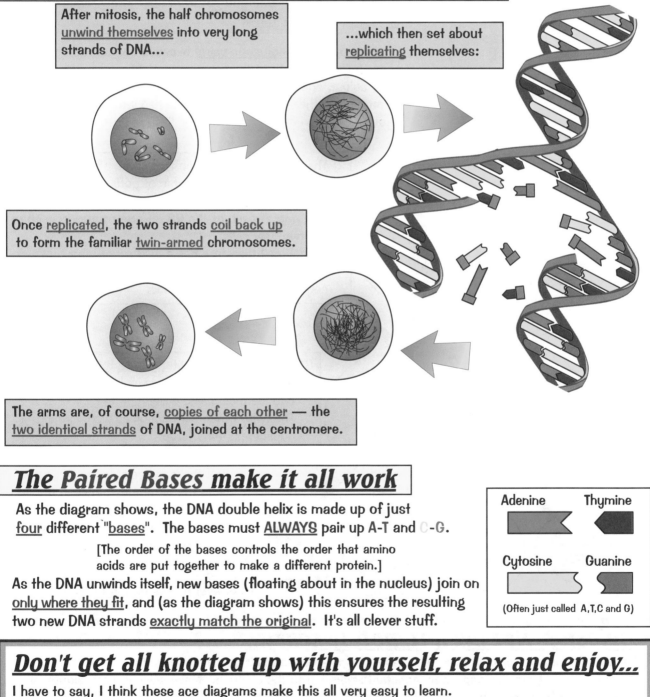

After mitosis, the half chromosomes unwind themselves into very long strands of DNA...

...which then set about replicating themselves:

Once replicated, the two strands coil back up to form the familiar twin-armed chromosomes.

The arms are, of course, copies of each other — the two identical strands of DNA, joined at the centromere.

The Paired Bases make it all work

As the diagram shows, the DNA double helix is made up of just four different "bases". The bases must **ALWAYS** pair up A-T and C-G.

[The order of the bases controls the order that amino acids are put together to make a different protein.]

As the DNA unwinds itself, new bases (floating about in the nucleus) join on only where they fit, and (as the diagram shows) this ensures the resulting two new DNA strands exactly match the original. It's all clever stuff.

Adenine	Thymine
Cytosine	Guanine

(Often just called A,T,C and G)

Don't get all knotted up with yourself, relax and enjoy...

I have to say, I think these ace diagrams make this all very easy to learn.
You know the drill. Cover the page and scribble down the details of all three sections.

Gamete Production: Meiosis

You thought mitosis was exciting. Hah! You ain't seen nothing yet. <u>Meiosis</u> is the other type of cell division. It only happens in the <u>reproductive organs</u> (ovaries and testes).

> <u>Meiosis</u> produces <u>"cells which have half the proper number of chromosomes"</u>.
> Such cells are also known as <u>"haploid gametes"</u>.

These cells are "genetically different" from each other because the genes all get <u>shuffled up</u> during meiosis and each gamete only gets <u>half</u> of them, selected at random.
Confused? I'm not surprised. But fear not, coz...   ....well worse things happen at sea...
The diagrams below will make it a lot clearer — but you have to <u>study</u> them pretty hard.

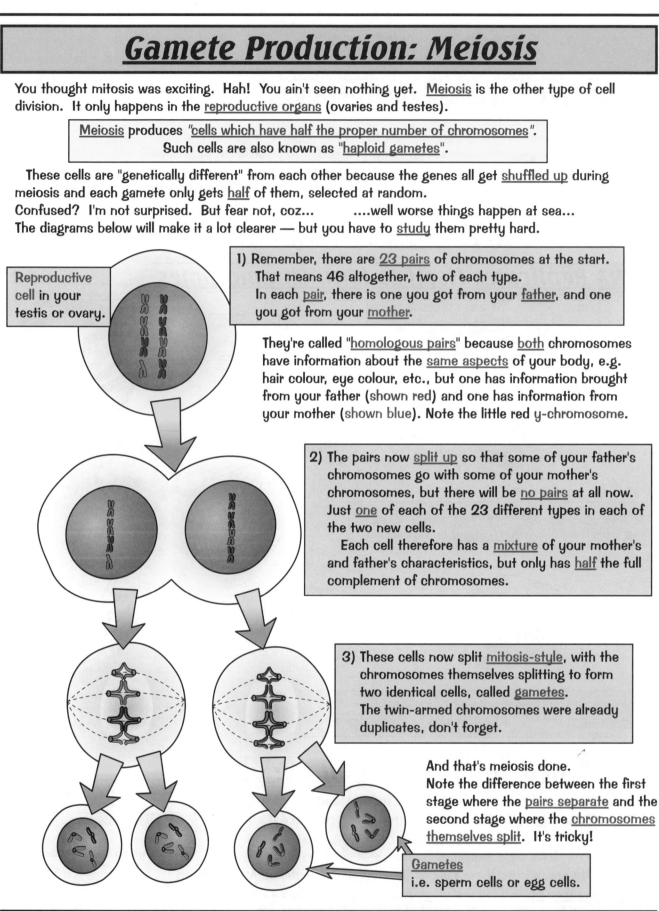

Reproductive cell in your testis or ovary.

1) Remember, there are <u>23 pairs</u> of chromosomes at the start. That means 46 altogether, two of each type.
In each <u>pair</u>, there is one you got from your <u>father</u>, and one you got from your <u>mother</u>.

They're called "<u>homologous pairs</u>" because <u>both</u> chromosomes have information about the <u>same aspects</u> of your body, e.g. hair colour, eye colour, etc., but one has information brought from your father (shown red) and one has information from your mother (shown blue). Note the little red y-chromosome.

2) The pairs now <u>split up</u> so that some of your father's chromosomes go with some of your mother's chromosomes, but there will be <u>no pairs</u> at all now. Just <u>one</u> of each of the 23 different types in each of the two new cells.
   Each cell therefore has a <u>mixture</u> of your mother's and father's characteristics, but only has <u>half</u> the full complement of chromosomes.

3) These cells now split <u>mitosis-style</u>, with the chromosomes themselves splitting to form two identical cells, called <u>gametes</u>.
The twin-armed chromosomes were already duplicates, don't forget.

And that's meiosis done.
Note the difference between the first stage where the <u>pairs separate</u> and the second stage where the <u>chromosomes themselves split</u>. It's tricky!

<u>Gametes</u>
i.e. sperm cells or egg cells.

Meiosis? Not even remotely scary...

There's a few tricky words in there which don't help — especially if you just ignore them...
The only way to <u>learn</u> this page is by constant reference to the diagram. Make sure you can sketch all the parts of it <u>from memory</u> and <u>scribble notes</u> to explain each stage. Even so, it's still difficult to understand it all, never mind remember it.   But that's what you gotta do!

Fertilisation: The Meeting of Gametes

There are 23 Pairs of Human Chromosomes

They are well known and numbered. In every <u>cell nucleus</u> we have <u>two</u> of each type. The diagram shows the 23 pairs of chromosomes from a human cell. <u>One</u> chromosome in <u>each pair</u> is inherited from each of our parents. Normal body cells have 46 chromosomes, in <u>23 homologous pairs</u>.

Remember, "<u>homologous</u>" means that the two chromosomes in each pair are <u>equivalent</u> to each other. In other words, the number 19 chromosomes from both your parents <u>pair off together</u>, as do the number 17s etc. What you <u>don't get</u> is the number 12 chromosome from one parent pairing off with, say, the number 5 chromosome from the other.

Reproductive Cells undergo Meiosis to Produce Gametes:

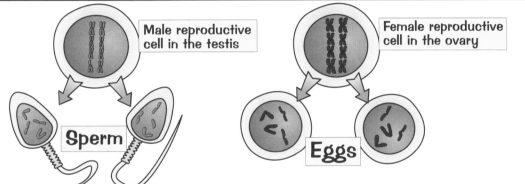

Male reproductive cell in the testis

Female reproductive cell in the ovary

Sperm

Eggs

The <u>gametes</u> remember, only have <u>one chromosome</u> to describe each bit of you, <u>one copy</u> of each of the chromosomes numbered 1 to 23. But a <u>normal cell</u> needs <u>two</u> chromosomes of each type — one from <u>each parent</u>, so...

Fertilisation is the Joining Together of the Gametes

Here's a mouthful of a <u>definition</u> for you to learn:

> FERTILISATION is the fusion of haploid male and female gametes, restoring the diploid number of chromosomes in a zygote.

Put simply fertilisation is when the <u>sperm</u> and the <u>egg</u>, with <u>23 chromosomes each</u>, join together to form an offspring with a full <u>46 chromosomes</u>. You've got to learn the posh <u>definition</u> though.

Fertilisation:

Gametes

sperm

egg

Zygote

fertilised egg

When the gametes <u>FUSE</u> the 23 single chromosomes in one gamete <u>will all pair off</u> with their appropriate "partner chromosomes" from the other gamete to form the full 23 pairs again, No.4 with No.4, No.13 with No.13 etc. etc. Don't forget, the two chromosomes in a pair both contain the <u>same basic genes</u>, e.g. for hair colour, etc.

The resulting offspring will then receive its <u>outward characteristics</u> as a <u>mixture</u> from the <u>two</u> sets of chromosomes, so it will <u>inherit features</u> from <u>both parents</u>. Pretty cool, eh.

It should all be starting to come together now...

If you go through these last two pages you should see how the two processes, meiosis and fertilisation, are kind of opposite. Practise <u>sketching out</u> the sequence of diagrams, with notes, for both pages till it all sinks in. Nice, innit.

The Work of Mendel

Mendel's Pea Plant Experiments

Gregor Mendel was an Austrian monk who trained in mathematics and natural history at the University of Vienna. On his garden plot at the monastery, Mendel noted how characteristics in plants were passed on from one generation to the next. The results of his research became the foundation of modern genetics.

The diagrams show two <u>crosses for height</u> in pea plants that Mendel carried out...

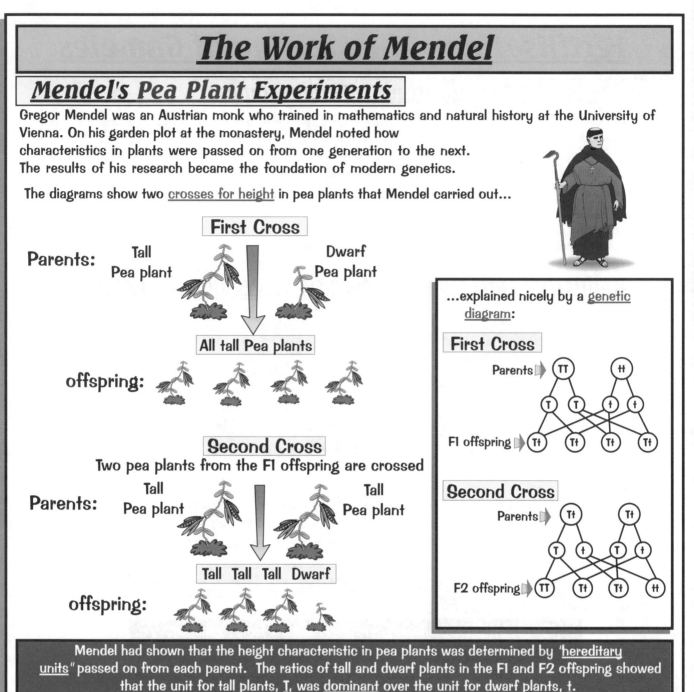

Mendel had shown that the height characteristic in pea plants was determined by "<u>hereditary units</u>" passed on from each parent. The ratios of tall and dwarf plants in the F1 and F2 offspring showed that the unit for tall plants, <u>T</u>, was <u>dominant</u> over the unit for dwarf plants, <u>t</u>.

Mendel's Conclusions

Mendel reached these 3 important conclusions about <u>heredity in plants</u>:

1) Characteristics in plants are determined by "<u>hereditary units</u>".

2) Hereditary units are passed on from both parents, <u>one unit</u> from <u>each parent</u>.

3) Hereditary units can be <u>dominant</u> or <u>recessive</u> — if an individual has both the dominant and the recessive unit for a characteristic, the dominant characteristic will be expressed.

From the benefit of modern science we know that the "hereditary units" are of course <u>genes</u>. In Mendel's time this technology was not as advanced and the significance of his work was not to be realised until after his death.

Learn the facts then see what you know...

Mendel was a pretty clever chappy don't you think? Learn the details of the pea plant cross he did and the genetic diagram. It's quite straightforward, once you get familiar with it. <u>Learn the whole page</u>, then <u>cover it up</u> and <u>scribble it out</u>. They're bound to ask you about old rogues like Gregor.

Girl or Boy? — X and Y Chromosomes

There are 23 matched pairs of chromosomes in every human cell. You'll notice the 23rd pair are labelled XY. They're the two chromosomes that decide whether you turn out <u>male or female</u>. They're called the X and Y chromosomes because they look like an X and a Y.

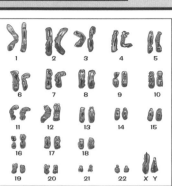

> <u>All men</u> have <u>an X</u> and <u>a Y</u> chromosome: XY
> <u>The Y chromosome is dominant</u> and causes <u>male characteristics</u>.
>
> <u>All women</u> have <u>two X chromosomes</u>: XX
> The XX combination allows <u>female characteristics</u> to develop.

The diagram below shows the way the male XY chromosomes and female XX chromosomes split up to form the <u>gametes</u> (eggs or sperms), and then combine together at <u>fertilisation</u>.

The criss–cross lines show all the <u>possible</u> ways the X and Y chromosomes <u>could</u> combine.
Remember, <u>only one of these</u> would actually happen for any offspring.
What the diagram shows us is the <u>relative probability</u> of each type of zygote (offspring) occurring.

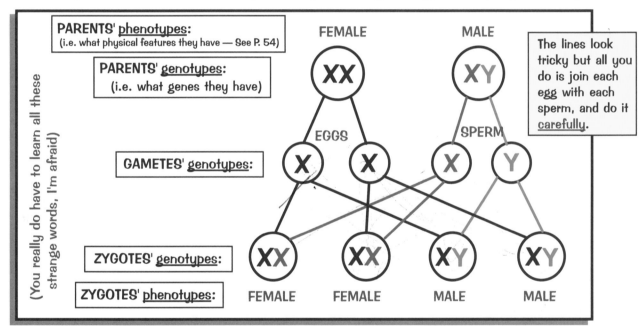

The other way of doing this is with a <u>checkerboard</u> type diagram. If you don't understand how it works, ask "Teach" to explain it. The <u>pairs of letters</u> in the middle show the <u>genotypes</u> of the possible offspring.

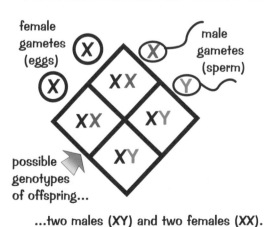

...two males (XY) and two females (XX).

Both diagrams show that there'll be the same proportion of male and female offspring, because there are <u>two XX results</u> and <u>two XY results</u>.

Don't forget that this <u>50:50 ratio</u> is only a <u>probability</u>. If you had four kids they <u>could</u> all be <u>boys</u> — yes I know, terrifying isn't it.

How can it take all that just to say it's a 50:50 chance...

Make sure you know all about X and Y chromosomes and who has what combination.
The diagrams are real important. Practise reproducing them until you can do it <u>effortlessly</u>.

Section Five — Genetics and Evolution

Monohybrid Crosses: Terminology

"Hey man, like *monohybrid crosses*, yeah right... ...so like, *what does it mean*, man?"   Just this, pal:

Breeding <u>two plants</u> or <u>animals</u>, who have <u>one gene different</u>, to see what you <u>get</u>.

It's always best done with a diagram like either of these:

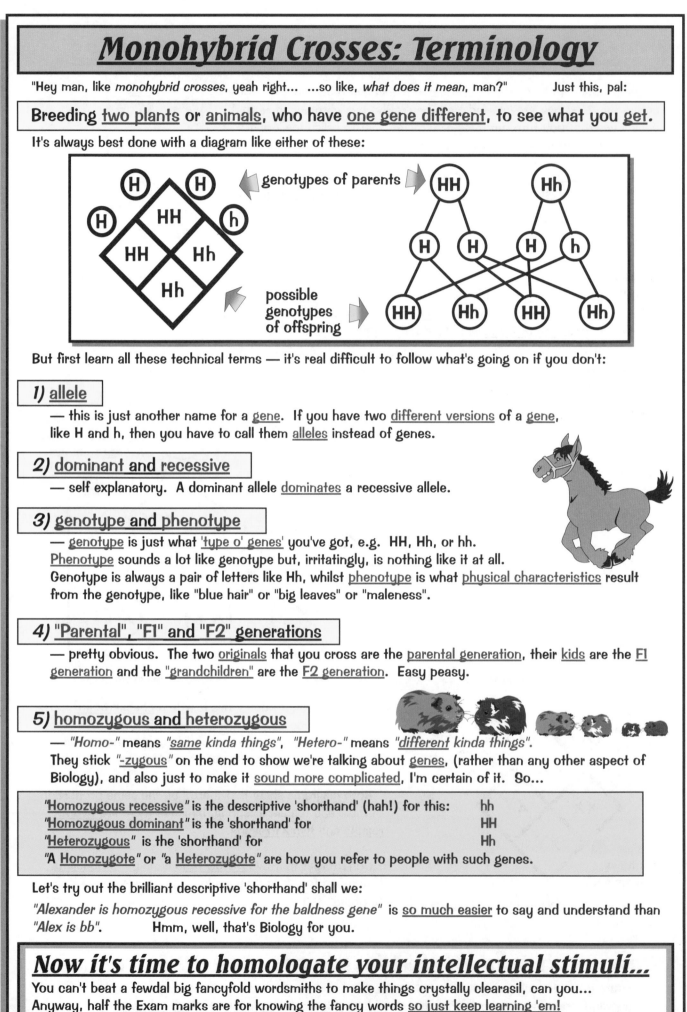

But first learn all these technical terms — it's real difficult to follow what's going on if you don't:

1) <u>allele</u>

— this is just another name for a <u>gene</u>. If you have two <u>different versions</u> of a <u>gene</u>, like H and h, then you have to call them <u>alleles</u> instead of genes.

2) <u>dominant and recessive</u>

— self explanatory. A dominant allele <u>dominates</u> a recessive allele.

3) <u>genotype and phenotype</u>

— <u>genotype</u> is just what <u>'type o' genes'</u> you've got, e.g. HH, Hh, or hh. <u>Phenotype</u> sounds a lot like genotype but, irritatingly, is nothing like it at all. Genotype is always a pair of letters like Hh, whilst <u>phenotype</u> is what <u>physical characteristics</u> result from the genotype, like "blue hair" or "big leaves" or "maleness".

4) <u>"Parental", "F1" and "F2" generations</u>

— pretty obvious. The two <u>originals</u> that you cross are the <u>parental generation</u>, their <u>kids</u> are the <u>F1 generation</u> and the <u>"grandchildren"</u> are the <u>F2 generation</u>. Easy peasy.

5) <u>homozygous and heterozygous</u>

— *"Homo-"* means *"<u>same kinda things</u>"*, *"Hetero-"* means *"<u>different</u> kinda things"*. They stick <u>"-zygous"</u> on the end to show we're talking about <u>genes</u>, (rather than any other aspect of Biology), and also just to make it <u>sound more complicated</u>, I'm certain of it. So...

<u>"Homozygous recessive"</u> is the descriptive 'shorthand' (hah!) for this:	hh
<u>"Homozygous dominant"</u> is the 'shorthand' for	HH
<u>"Heterozygous"</u> is the 'shorthand' for	Hh
"A <u>Homozygote</u>" or "a <u>Heterozygote</u>" are how you refer to people with such genes.	

Let's try out the brilliant descriptive 'shorthand' shall we:

"Alexander is homozygous recessive for the baldness gene" is <u>so much easier</u> to say and understand than *"Alex is bb"*.   Hmm, well, that's Biology for you.

<u>Now it's time to homologate your intellectual stimuli...</u>

You can't beat a fewdal big fancyfold wordsmiths to make things crystally clearasil, can you... Anyway, half the Exam marks are for knowing the fancy words <u>so just keep learning 'em!</u>

Monohybrid Crosses: Hamsters

Cross-breeding Hamsters

It can be all too easy to find yourself cross-breeding hamsters, some with normal hair and a mild disposition and others with wild scratty hair and a leaning towards crazy acrobatics.

Let's say that the gene which causes the crazy nature is _recessive_, so we use a _small "h"_ for it, whilst normal (boring) behaviour is due to a _dominant gene_, so we represent it with a _capital "H"_.
1) A _crazy hamster_ must have the _genotype_: hh.
2) However, a _normal hamster_ can have _two possible genotypes_: HH or Hh.
   This is pretty important — it's the basic difference between dominant and recessive genes:

> To display _recessive characteristics_ you must have
> _both alleles recessive_, hh, (i.e. be "homozygous recessive")
>
> But to display _dominant characteristics_ you can be _either_
> HH ("homozygous dominant") or Hh ("heterozygous").

It's only that difference which makes monohybrid crosses even _remotely_ interesting.   If hh gave crazy hamsters, HH gave normal hamsters and Hh something in between, it'd all be pretty dull.

An Almost Unbearably Exciting Example

Let's take a thoroughbred crazy hamster, genotype hh, with a thoroughbred normal hamster, genotype HH, and cross breed them. You must learn this whole diagram thoroughly, till you can do it all yourself:

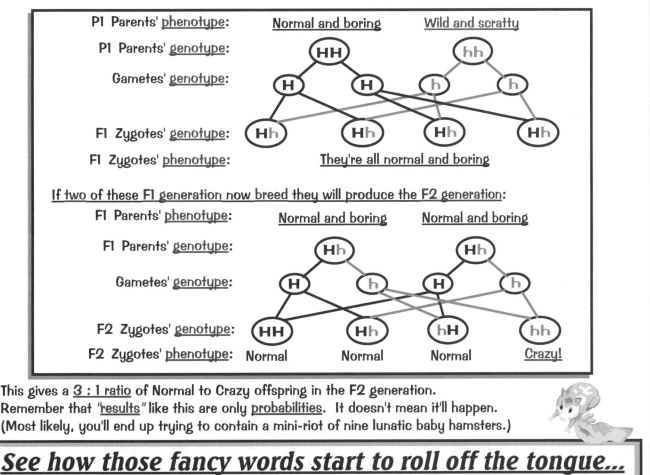

This gives a _3 : 1 ratio_ of Normal to Crazy offspring in the F2 generation.
Remember that "results" like this are only _probabilities_. It doesn't mean it'll happen.
(Most likely, you'll end up trying to contain a mini-riot of nine lunatic baby hamsters.)

See how those fancy words start to roll off the tongue...

The diagram and all its fancy words need to be second nature to you. So practise writing it out _from memory_ until you get it all right. Because when you can do one — _you can do 'em all_.

Disorders Caused by Recessive Alleles

Cystic Fibrosis is caused by a Recessive Allele

1) *Cystic Fibrosis* is a genetic disorder which affects about *1 in 1600 people* in the UK.
2) It's *caused by a* defective gene which the person inherits from their parents.
   There's still no cure or effective treatment for this condition.
3) The result of the defective gene is that the body produces a lot of thick sticky mucus in the lungs,
   which has to be removed by massage.
4) Excess mucous also occurs in the pancreas, causing digestive problems.
5) Much more seriously though, the blockage of the air passages in the lungs causes a lot of chest
   infections.
6) Physiotherapy and antibiotics clear them up but slowly the sufferer becomes more and more ill.

The genetics behind cystic fibrosis is actually very straightforward.
The gene which causes cystic fibrosis is a recessive gene, c, carried by about 1 person in 20.
If both parents are carriers there is a 1 in 4 chance of their child being a sufferer as shown here:

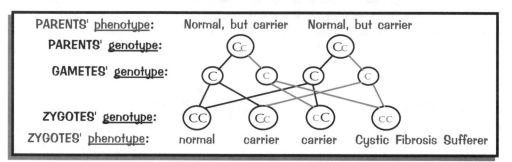

PARENTS' phenotype:	Normal, but carrier	Normal, but carrier
PARENTS' genotype:	Cc	Cc
GAMETES' genotype:	C c	C c
ZYGOTES' genotype:	CC Cc	cC cc
ZYGOTES' phenotype:	normal carrier	carrier Cystic Fibrosis Sufferer

Sickle Cell Anaemia

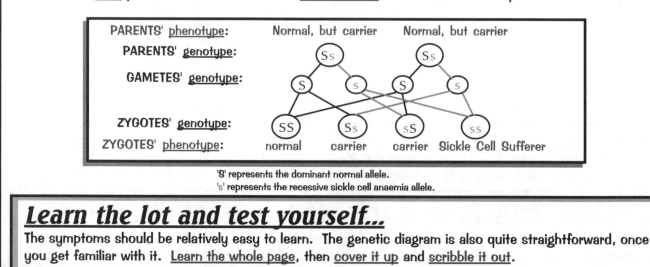

normal cell   sickle cell

1) This disorder causes the red blood cells to be shaped like sickles
   instead of the normal round shape.
2) They then get stuck in the capillaries which deprives body cells of oxygen.
3) It's an unpleasant, painful disorder and sufferers are at risk of dying
   at an early age.
4) Sickle cell anaemia is rare in Britain, but not in some African countries.
5) This is because carriers of the recessive allele which causes it are more immune to malaria. Hence,
   being a carrier increases their chance of survival in some parts of the world, even though some of their
   offspring are going to suffer from sickle cell anaemia.
6) The genetics are identical to Cystic Fibrosis because both disorders are caused by a recessive allele.
   Hence if both parents are carriers there's a 1 in 4 chance each child will develop it:

PARENTS' phenotype:	Normal, but carrier	Normal, but carrier
PARENTS' genotype:	Ss	Ss
GAMETES' genotype:	S s	S s
ZYGOTES' genotype:	SS Ss	sS ss
ZYGOTES' phenotype:	normal carrier	carrier Sickle Cell Sufferer

'S' represents the dominant normal allele.
's' represents the recessive sickle cell anaemia allele.

Learn the lot and test yourself...

The symptoms should be relatively easy to learn. The genetic diagram is also quite straightforward, once
you get familiar with it. Learn the whole page, then cover it up and scribble it out.

Disorders Caused by Dominant Alleles

Huntington's Chorea is caused by a Dominant Allele

1) <u>Unlike</u> Cystic Fibrosis this disorder is caused by a <u>dominant allele</u>.

2) This results in a <u>50% chance</u> of each child inheriting the disorder if just <u>one parent</u> is a carrier. These are seriously grim odds.

3) The "<u>carrier</u>" parent will of course be a <u>sufferer</u> too since the allele is dominant, but the symptoms do not appear until after the age of 40, by which time the allele has been passed on to <u>children</u> and even <u>grandchildren</u>. Hence the disorder persists.

4) The disorder isn't nice, resulting in shaking, erratic body movements and severe mental deterioration.

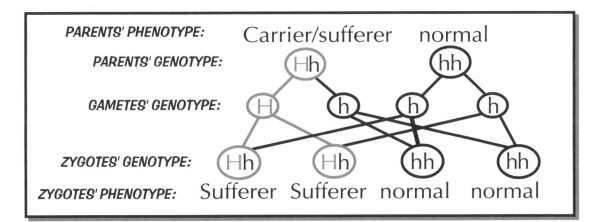

Note: <u>If</u> one parent is a <u>sufferer</u>, there's a <u>2 in 4 chance</u> of each of her children having the disorder.

Polydactyly

1) Polydactyly is a disorder that causes the person to have <u>extra fingers</u> and <u>extra toes</u>. The most common form of polydactyly is an extra little finger.

2) It's caused by a <u>dominant allele</u> which means the genetic diagrams are the same as Huntington's Chorea. The disorder isn't fatal and doesn't affect reproduction so sufferers pass on the Polydactyly genes to their children as follows:

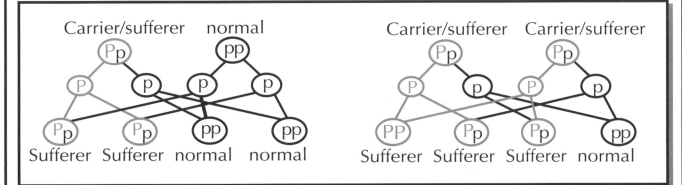

3) There's a <u>50%</u> chance of each child inheriting the disorder if just <u>one parent</u> is a carrier and a <u>75%</u> chance if both parents are carriers.

Learn the facts then see what you know...

There are various ways they could test your knowledge of a genetic disease in the Exam. The numbered facts are relatively easy marks. For trickier questions you'll need to be able to easily reproduce any of the stuff in the white boxes. So practise <u>learning and understanding</u> it till you can.

Mutations

Mutation sounds like a word to mean only bad things... and most of the time it is, but mutations are also what makes evolution happen — without them we'd still be goo in the primordial soup. No exams though.

Mutations Show up as a Strange New Characteristic

1) A mutation occurs when an organism develops with some strange new characteristic that no other member of the species has had before.

2) For example if someone was born with blue hair it would be caused by a mutation.

3) Some mutations are beneficial, but most are disastrous (e.g. blue hair).

Mutations are...

...just this:

> A MUTATION is a change in a gene, DNA or the number of chromosomes in a cell which leads to genetic variation.

← Learn it

There are several ways that mutations happen, but in the end they're all down to faulty DNA.

Mutations usually happen when the DNA is replicating itself and something goes wrong.

Radiation and Certain Chemicals cause Mutations

Mutations occur "naturally", probably caused by "natural" background radiation (from the sun and rocks etc.) or just the laws of chance that every now and then a chromosomes doesn't quite copy itself properly. However the chance of mutation is increased by exposing yourself:

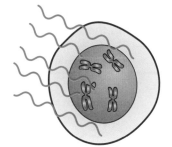

1) To nuclear radiation, i.e. alpha, beta and gamma radiation. This is sometimes called ionising radiation because it creates ions (charged particles) as it passes through stuff. (See the Physics Book.)

2) To X-rays and Ultra-Violet light, which are the highest-frequency parts of the electromagnetic spectrum (together with gamma rays).

No no! not me!

3) To certain chemicals which are known to cause mutations. Such chemicals are called mutagens! If the mutations produce cancer then the chemicals are often called carcinogens.

4) Cigarette smoke contains chemical mutagens (or carcinogens)... (I'm sayin' nowt — See P. 49.)

Don't get your genes in a twist, this stuff's easy...

There are three sections with numbered points for each. Memorise the headings and learn the numbered points, then cover the page and scribble down everything you can remember.

I know it makes your head hurt, but every time you try to remember the stuff, the more it sinks in. It'll all be worth it in the end. Smile and enjoy.

Mutations

Most Mutations are Harmful

If a mutation occurs in <u>reproductive cells</u>, then the young may develop <u>abnormally</u> or <u>die</u> at an early stage of their development.

Mutations Often Cause Cancer

If a mutation occurs in body cells, the mutant cells may start to <u>multiply</u> in an <u>uncontrolled</u> way and <u>invade</u> other parts of the body. This is what we know as <u>cancer</u>.

Some Mutations are Beneficial, giving us "EVOLUTION"

1) Blue "<u>budgies</u>" appeared suddenly as a mutation amongst yellow budgies. This is a good example of a <u>neutral effect</u>. It didn't harm its chances of survival and so it flourished (and at one stage, every grandma in Britain had one).

2) <u>Very occasionally</u>, a mutation will give the organism a survival <u>advantage</u> over its relatives, and it may well live on in conditions where the others die. This is <u>natural selection</u> and <u>evolution</u> at work.

3) A good example is a mutation in a bacteria that makes it <u>resistant to antibiotics</u>, so the mutant gene <u>lives on</u>, in the offspring, creating a <u>resistant "strain"</u> of bacteria, which antibiotics will not kill.
We then have to develop a new antibiotic to deal with the new resistant strain of bacteria. And so it goes on.

Down's Syndrome is Caused by a Mutation

1) This is a <u>completely different</u> type of genetic disorder where a person ends up with <u>three chromosome 21s</u> in their cells.

2) Down's Syndrome is actually an example of a <u>mutation</u>. It is unlike most mutations which involve changes to genes. This one just involves having an <u>extra chromosome</u>.

3) The problem happens in one of the woman's ovaries. Occasionally <u>both chromosome 21s</u> go into the same egg cell, leaving the other with none. If the egg with two chromosome 21s is fertilised the resulting offspring will have <u>three</u> chromosome 21s.

4) This causes Down's Syndrome.

20   21   22

The main effects of Down's Syndrome are:
a) The child will have <u>lower mental ability</u>.
b) They are also generally <u>more susceptible to certain diseases</u>.

Learn the facts then see what you know...

There are three sections on this page, with several numbered points in each. You need to <u>learn</u> all these details about the harmful effects of mutations, including Down's Syndrome.
When you think you know it all, <u>cover the page</u> and <u>scribble it all down</u> again. Then check back and see what important points you missed. Remember, they could ask any of this stuff.

Natural Selection

Darwin's Theory of Natural Selection is Ace

1) This theory is cool and is a big step towards a comprehensive explanation for all life on Earth.

2) Mind you, it caused some trouble at the time, because for the first time ever, there was a highly plausible explanation for our own existence, without the need for a "Creator".

3) This was bad news for the religious authorities of the time, who tried to ridicule old Charlie's ideas. But, as they say, "the truth will out".

Darwin made Four Important Observations...

1) All organisms produce more offspring than could possibly survive.

2) But in fact, population numbers tend to remain fairly constant over long periods of time.

3) Organisms in a species show wide variation (due to different genes).

4) Some of the variations are inherited and passed on to the next generation.

...and then made these Two Deductions:

1) Since most offspring don't survive, all organisms must have to struggle for survival. (Being eaten, disease and competition cause large numbers of individuals to die.)

2) The ones who survive and reproduce will pass on their genes.

This is the famous "Survival of the fittest" statement. Organisms with slightly less survival-value will probably perish first, leaving the strongest and fittest to pass on their genes to the next generation.

Mutations play a big part in Natural Selection...

...by creating a new feature with a high survival value. Once upon a time maybe all rabbits had short ears and managed OK. Then one day out popped a mutant with big ears who was always the first to dive for cover. Pretty soon he's got a whole family of them with big ears, all diving for cover before the other rabbits, and before you know it there're only big-eared rabbits left because the rest just didn't hear trouble coming quick enough.   *(Eat your heart out, Rudyard Kipling)*

FOX!

Natural Selection

Horrible Example 1 — Flat Cockroaches

A recent creepy crawly example of <u>evolution</u> through <u>natural selection</u> is all too apparent in many kitchens around the world.

1) As health inspectors wage war on them, little do they realise how much the <u>cockroach</u> has gone out of its way to fit in.

2) Over the centuries, as man and cockroaches have <u>shared accommodation</u> the cockroaches have actually become <u>smaller and flatter</u> to adapt to our domestic environment.

3) In each generation the smaller, flatter offspring find <u>easier access</u> to our larders and <u>more places to hide</u>, while the <u>larger</u>, <u>bulkier</u> offspring get squashed out.

Scary Example 2: Bacteria Adapt to beat Antibiotics

The "<u>survival of the fittest</u>" affects bacteria just the same as other living things. The trouble is that we're giving them all the help they need to get more and more resistant to our bacterial weapons — antibiotics.

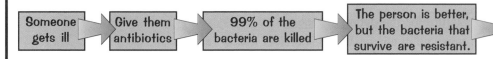

| Someone gets ill | → | Give them antibiotics | → | 99% of the bacteria are killed | → | The person is better, but the bacteria that survive are resistant. | → | If the resistant bacteria get passed on and thrive in someone else, the antibiotics won't help them. |

Overuse of antibiotics is making things worse:

1) Nowadays people <u>expect</u> to get antibiotics for colds and throat infections and stuff.

2) The doctor gives them antibiotics <u>in case</u> it's a bacterial infection.

3) This produces <u>resistant</u> bacteria as shown above.

4) When a resistant bacteria arrives, we have to invent <u>new antibiotics</u> and then the process happens again.

5) Nowadays bacteria are getting resistant at such a rate the development of antibiotics <u>can't keep up</u>. Eeek!

All Wild Creatures live in a very Harsh World indeed...

The natural world may seem like a paradise on Earth to a lot of people, but the reality for the wild creatures that live in it is quite different.

The natural world is in fact a very harsh environment where many offspring <u>die young</u>, due to <u>predators</u>, <u>disease</u> and <u>competition</u>.

But remember, this is an important element in the process of <u>natural selection</u>. There has to be <u>a large surplus of offspring</u> for nature to <u>select the fittest</u> from.

Farms are Much Easier...

Life for any <u>farm animal</u> is a veritable dream compared to the "<u>eat or be eaten</u>" savage reality of the 'natural' world.

Most wild animals are eventually either <u>eaten alive</u> or else they <u>starve to death</u>. Think about it — <u>they've all gotta go somehow</u>. Give them a nice cosy civilised farm any day, I say...

"Natural Selection" — sounds like Vegan Chocolates...

These two pages are split into five sections. <u>Memorise</u> the headings, then <u>cover the page</u> and <u>scribble down</u> all you can about each section. Keep trying until you can <u>remember</u> all the important points.

Fossils

Fossils are the "remains" of plants and animals which lived millions of years ago.

There are Three ways that Fossils can be Formed:

1) FROM THE hard parts OF ANIMALS   (Most fossils happen this way.)

Things like bones, teeth, shells, etc, which don't decay easily, can last a long
time when buried. They're eventually replaced by minerals as they decay,
forming a rock-like substance shaped like the original hard part. The
surrounding sediments also turn to rock, but the fossil stays distinct inside the
rock, and eventually someone digs it up.

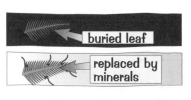
buried leaf

replaced by
minerals

2) FROM THE softer parts OF ANIMALS OR PLANTS — petrification

Sometimes fossils are formed from the softer parts which somehow
haven't decayed. The soft material gradually becomes "petrified" (turns to
stone) as it slowly decays and is replaced by minerals. This is rare, since
there are very few occasions when decay occurs so slowly.

3) IN PLACES WHERE no decay HAPPENS

The whole original plant or animal may survive for thousands of years:

a) Amber — no oxygen or moisture for the decay microbes.
Insects are often found fully preserved in amber, which is a clear yellow "stone"
made of fossilised resin that ran out of an ancient tree hundreds of millions of
years ago, engulfing the insect.

b) Glaciers — too cold for the decay microbes to work.
A hairy mammoth was found fully preserved in a glacier somewhere
several years ago (at least that's what I heard, though I never saw any pictures
of it so maybe it was a hoax, I'm not really sure, but anyway in principle one could
turn up any time...)

c) Waterlogged bogs — too acidic for decay microbes.
A 10,000 year old man was found in a bog a few years ago.
He was dead, and a bit squashed but otherwise quite well
preserved, although it was clear he had been murdered.
(Police are not looking for any witnesses and have asked anyone *else*
who thinks they may have important information to just keep away.)

Evidence from Rock and Soil Strata

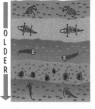

The fossils found in rock layers tell us two things:

1) What the creatures and plants looked like.
2) How long ago they existed, by the type of rock they're in. Generally speaking,
   the deeper you find the fossil, the older it will be, though of course rocks get
   pushed upwards and eroded, so very old rocks can become exposed.

Fossils are usually dated by geologists who already know the age of the rock. The Grand Canyon in
Arizona is about 1 mile deep. It was formed by a river slowly cutting down through layers of rock. The
rocks at the bottom are about 1,000,000,000 years old, and the fossil record in the sides is pretty cool.

Don't get bogged down in all this information...

Make sure you're fully aware of the three different types of fossil and how they're formed.
Also make sure you learn all the details about what information rocks provide. Many people read stuff
and then think they know it. It's only if you cover it up that you find out what you really know.

Section Five — Genetics and Evolution

Evolution

The Theory of Evolution is Cool

1) This suggests that all the animals and plants on Earth gradually "evolved" over millions of years, rather than just suddenly popping into existence. Makes sense.

2) Life on Earth began as simple organisms from which all the more complex organisms evolved. And it only took about 3,000,000,000 years.

Fossils Provide Evidence for it

1) Fossils provide lots of evidence for evolution.
2) They show how today's species have changed and developed over millions of years.
3) There are quite a few "missing links" though because the fossil record is incomplete.
4) This is because very very few dead plants or animals actually turn into fossils.
5) Most just decay away completely.

Darwin's Finches evolved to suit different islands

Darwin's finches are a fine example of how evolution occurs...

1) When Darwin went to the Galapagos Islands, he saw that many of the islands had their own unique species of finch.
2) Each finch had a beak and body well adapted to the kind of food found on its particular island.
3) The finches were different species, but they all looked very similar.
4) Darwin realised that the finches had evolved from a common ancestor.
5) He proposed that originally a few seed-eating finches had flown to the islands from the mainland. Over millions of years the finches adapted to the foods available on each island — and evolved into separate species.

 Buds and Fruit Eater  Seed Eater  Grub and Insect Eater  Insect Eater

Extinction is Pretty Bad News

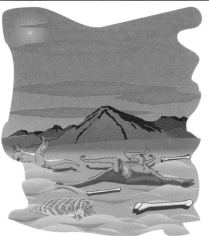

The dinosaurs and hairy mammoths became extinct and it's only fossils that tell us they ever existed at all, (notwithstanding the odd questionable glacier story).

There are three ways a species can become extinct:
1) The environment changes too quickly.
2) A new predator or disease kills them all.
3) They can't compete with another (new) species for food.

As the environment slowly changes, it will gradually favour certain new characteristics amongst the members of the species and over many generations those features will proliferate. In this way, the species constantly adapts to its changing environment. But if the environment changes too fast the whole species may be wiped out, i.e. extinction...

Stop horsing around and just learn the facts...

Another stupefyingly easy page to learn. Use the mini-essay method. Just make sure you learn every fact, that's all. Dinosaurs never did proper revision and look what happened to them. (Mind you they did last about 200 million years, which is about 199.9 million more than we have, so far...)

Selective Breeding

Selective Breeding is Very Simple

Selective breeding is also called artificial selection, because humans artificially select the plants or animals that are going to breed and flourish, according to what we want from them.
This is the basic process involved in selective breeding:

1) From your existing stock select the ones which have the best characteristics.

2) Breed them with each other.

3) Select the best of the offspring, and combine them with the best that you already have and breed again.

4) Continue this process over several generations to develop the desired traits.

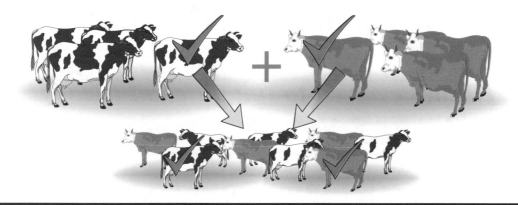

Selective Breeding is Very Useful in Farming

Artificial selection like this is used in most areas of modern farming, to great benefit:

1) Better beef

Selectively breeding beef cattle to get the best beef (taste, texture, appearance, etc).

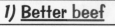

2) Better milk

Selectively breeding milking cows to increase milk yield and resistance to disease.

3) Better chickens

Selectively breeding chickens to improve egg size and number of eggs per hen.

4) Better wheat

Selectively breeding wheat to produce new varieties with better yields and better disease-resistance too.

5) Better flowers

Selectively breeding flowers to produce bigger and better and more colourful ones.

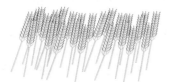

Selective Breeding

The Main Drawback is a Reduction in the Gene Pool

In farming, animals are selectively bred to develop the best features, which are basically:

A) <u>Maximum Yield</u> of meat, milk, grain etc.

B) <u>Good Health</u> and <u>Disease Resistance</u>.

1) But selective breeding reduces the <u>number of alleles</u> in a population because the farmer keeps breeding from the "best" animals or plants — the same ones all the time.

2) This can cause serious problems if a <u>new disease appears</u>, as all the plants or animals could be wiped out.

3) This is made more likely because all the stock are <u>closely related</u> to each other, so if one of them is going to be killed by a new disease, the others are also likely to succumb to it.

> Oh Eck!

| Selective Breeding | → | Reduction in the number of different alleles (genes) | → | Less chance of any resistant alleles being present in the population | → | Nothing to selectively breed a new strain from |

Selective Breeding in Pedigree Dogs Causes Bad Health

Most of the above <u>doesn't apply</u> to selective breeding in <u>pedigree dogs</u> where <u>physical appearance</u> is the <u>only thing</u> that seems to matter — purely for winning dog shows. Many pedigree dogs (in fact <u>most</u> pedigree dogs) have quite bad <u>health problems</u> because of this artificial selection.

Random Cross-Breeds Can be Much Healthier Dogs

1) Mongrels (random cross-breeds) on the other hand, are usually much <u>healthier</u>, <u>fitter</u> dogs because they're not so <u>interbred</u>.

2) They're very often much nicer natured and they can be real pretty too.

3) The word <u>"mongrel"</u> does them no justice at all. If you want a really great dog, my advice is go to the dog rescue place and get a crazy cross-breed and just love him.

Don't sit there brooding over it, just learn the info...

<u>Selective breeding is a very simple topic</u>. In the Exam they'll likely give you half a page explaining how a farmer in Sussex did this or that with his crops or cows, and then they'll suddenly ask: "<u>What is meant by selective breeding?</u>" That's when you just write down the four points at the top of page 72. Then they'll ask you to "<u>Suggest other ways that selective breeding might be used by farmers in Sussex to improve their yield</u>". That's when you just list some of the examples that you've learnt.

They do like padding the questions out, don't they! In Olden Times (the 1970s) they would just have said: "<u>Explain what selective breeding is and give four examples of where it is used. — 8 Marks</u>" (!)

Cloning

Learn this definition of clones:

Clones are genetically identical organisms

Clones occur naturally in both plants and animals. Identical twins are clones of each other.
These days clones are very much a part of the high-tech farming industry.

Embryo Transplants in Cows

Normally, farmers only breed from their best cows and bulls. However, such traditional methods would
only allow the prize cow to produce one new offspring each year. These days the whole process has been
transformed using embryo transplants:

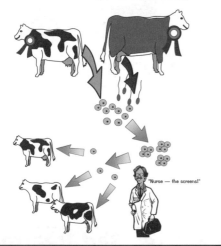

"Nurse — the screens!"

1) Sperm are taken from the prize bull.

2) They're checked for genetic defects and which sex they are.

3) They can also be frozen and used at a later date.

4) Selected prize cows are given hormones to
   make them produce lots of eggs.

5) The cows are then artificially inseminated.

6) The Embryos are taken from the prize cows
   and checked for sex and genetic defects.

7) The embryos are developed and split
   (to form clones) before any cells become specialised.

8) These embryos are implanted into other cows, where
   they grow. They can also be frozen and used at a later date.

Advantages of embryo transplants:
   a) Hundreds of "ideal" offspring can be produced every year from the best bull and cow.
   b) The original prize cow can keep producing prize eggs all year round.
Disadvantages:
   Only the usual drawback with clones — a reduced "gene pool" leading to vulnerability to new diseases.

The Essentials of Commercial Plant Cloning:

Tissue Culture

This is where, instead of starting
with at least a stem and bud, they
just put a few plant cells in a
growth medium with hormones and
it just grows into a new plant. Just
like that! Phew.

Parent plant

Cells removed from
the tip of the plant

Cells placed on a jelly
containing growth hormones

Hundreds of
clones can be
made from
just one
parent plant

Advantages of tissue culture:

1) Very fast — can produce thousands of plantlets in a few weeks.
2) Very little space needed.
3) Can grow all year — no problem with weather or seasons.
4) New plants are disease-free.
5) New plants can be developed (very quickly) by splicing new genes into plantlets and seeing how they turn out.

Disadvantages of Tissue culture:

Only the usual drawback with clones — a reduced "gene pool" leading to vulnerability to new diseases.

Stop Cloning Around and just learn it...

I hope you realise that they could easily test your knowledge of any sentence on this page. I only put in
stuff you need to know, you know. Practise scribbling out all the facts on this page, mini-essay style.

Genetic Engineering

Genetic Engineering is Ace — hopefully

This is a new science with exciting possibilities, but dangers too. The basic idea is to move sections of DNA (genes) from one organism to another so that it produces useful biological products. We presently use bacteria to produce human insulin for diabetes sufferers and also to produce human growth hormone for children who aren't growing properly.

Genetic Engineering involves these Important Stages:

1) The useful gene is "cut" from the DNA of, say, a human.
2) This is done using restriction enzymes.
   Particular enzymes will cut out particular bits of DNA.
3) Enzymes are then used to cut the DNA of a bacterium and the human gene is then inserted.
4) This "splicing" of a new gene is controlled by ligase enzymes.
5) The bacterium is now cultivated and soon there are millions of similar bacteria all producing, say, human insulin.
6) This can be done on an industrial scale and the useful product can be separated out.

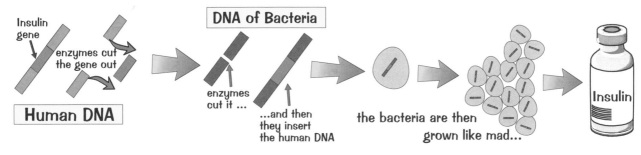

Hence we've turned nasty old bacteria into a useful biological factory.
Phew, that's modern science for you.

Using Animals as Chemists

1) The same approach can also be used to transfer useful genes into animal embryos. Sheep for example can be developed which produce useful substances (i.e. drugs) in their milk! This is a very easy way to produce drugs...

2) Insects also have their uses. Mosquitos may, in the near future, be used to combat diseases such as "malaria". The mosquitos that normally spread malaria are being genetically engineered to produce the malaria vaccine. Therefore instead of giving the disease to people they will soon hopefully be immunising them instead.

Nothing's been done to stop the itching though.

Hmmph... Kids these days, they're all the same...

Once again, they could ask you about any of the details on this page. The only way to be sure you know it: cover the page and write mini-essays on both topics. Then see what you missed, and try again...

Issues in Genetics

Science isn't just about cold hard facts any more. There's loads of stuff about whether or not the science is right or wrong. This <u>moral question stuff</u> is all lumped together and called "<u>ethical issues</u>". No matter what you believe, to get the marks for a question on this, you've <u>got to learn</u> what the different issues are:

Selective Breeding or Playing God

At the moment selective breeding is allowed in law so it must be OK?
Not everyone thinks so. Learn what the issues are and the examples given.

1) Some people think it's wrong to <u>manipulate</u> nature to force the evolution of animals for our benefit only.

2) For example to produce cows that would <u>die</u> if we didn't milk them, because we've <u>bred them</u> to produce too much milk. Or to breed pigs with so much meat on them that they can't stand up. Some think it's <u>cruel and wrong</u> and others think it's just what we need to provide <u>nutritious food</u> at a cheap price.

3) At the moment there are no laws against selective breeding and most people see it as <u>normal</u> farming practice.

Cloning — Medical Breakthrough or a step too far

1) The biggest issue in cloning at the moment is the cloning of <u>human embryos</u>.

2) Several groups of scientists want to clone human embryos to get <u>replacement tissues</u> and <u>organs</u> for people who need them.

3) A lot of people die at the moment because transplanted organs are <u>rejected</u> by their bodies. Using organs from embryos cloned from themselves would save their lives.

4) Some countries (including <u>Britain</u> and <u>Japan</u>) have banned human cloning because they think it is <u>morally wrong</u>. People argue that to create a life for spare parts and then kill it is wrong. Even though a lot of countries allow <u>abortion</u> of embryos at this stage of life.

Genetic Engineering or Frankenstein's Monster

There are loads of issues to do with genetic engineering. Learn these four:

1) A big problem for the future of human genetic engineering is the "Designer baby" problem that's talked about on page 53.

2) Changing the genetic make-up of any organisms may affect ecosystems in ways laboratory testing <u>can't predict</u>.

3) Large seed corporations can make sure they get money every year by selling plants that <u>won't produce fertile seeds,</u> or by producing plants that only respond to <u>their</u> fertilisers.

4) Genetic engineering may also mean that we can produce crops that grow in places they wouldn't before, <u>saving lives</u> in droughts and opening up freezing climates to farming.

Barry played God in the nativity — but I was the star...

This ethical issue stuff is hard to get a handle on coz it's less facts and more opinion. Make sure you <u>learn</u> what the <u>issues</u> are <u>with examples</u>. When you get an ethical issue exam question that asks for your opinion, get all these points down first and then give your opinion.

Revision Summary for Section Five

Gee, all that business about genes and chromosomes and the like — it's all pretty serious stuff, don't you think? It takes a real effort to get your head round it all. There's too many big fancy words, for one thing. But there you go — life's tough and you've just gotta face up to it. Use these questions to find out what you know — and what you don't. Then look back and learn the bits you didn't know. Then try the questions again, and again...

1) What are the two types of variation? Describe their relative importance for plants and animals.
2) List four features of animals which aren't affected at all by environment, and four which are.
3) What is the Human Genome Project? Write down three good things and four bad things about it.
4) On P. 54 there are 18 fancy words to do with genetics. List them all — with explanations.
5) Draw a set of diagrams showing the relationship between: cell, nucleus, chromosomes, genes, DNA.
6) Give a definition of mitosis. Draw a set of diagrams showing what happens in mitosis.
7) What is asexual reproduction? Give a proper definition for it. How does it involve mitosis?
8) Genes are chemical instructions. Give details of exactly what instructions they give.
9) Draw a set of diagrams to show how single armed chromosomes become double armed ones.
10) What are the names of the four "bases"? How do they make DNA replication work so well?
11) Where does meiosis take place? What kind of cells does meiosis produce?
12) Draw out the sequence of diagrams showing what happens during meiosis.
13) How many pairs of chromosomes are there in a normal human cell nucleus?
14) What happens to the chromosome numbers during meiosis and then during fertilisation?
15) What are X and Y chromosomes to do with? Who has what combination?
16) Draw a genetic inheritance diagram to show how these genes are passed on.
17) What is meant by monohybrid crosses?
18) Give three examples of the wonderful genetics descriptive shorthand.
19) Starting with parental genotypes **HH** and **hh**, draw a full genetic inheritance diagram to show the eventual genotypes and phenotypes of the F1 and F2 generations (of hamsters).
20) List the symptoms and treatment of cystic fibrosis. What causes this disease?
21) Draw a genetics diagram to show the probability of a child being a sufferer.
22) Give the cause and symptoms of sickle cell anaemia. Why does it not die out?
23) Explain the grim odds for Huntington's Chorea. Explain why Down's Syndrome is a mutation.
24) Give four definitions of what a mutation is. List the four main causes of mutations.
25) Give an example of harmful, neutral and beneficial mutations.
26) What were Darwin's four observations and two deductions? Is it a cosy life for wild animals?
27) Describe fully the three ways that fossils can form. Give examples of each type.
28) Explain how fossils found in rocks support the theory of evolution. Refer to the horse.
29) Describe the basic procedure in selective breeding (of cows). Give five other examples.
30) What is the main drawback of selective breeding in a) farming b) pedigree dogs?
31) Write down all you know on cloned plants.
32) Give a good account of embryo transplants, and a good account of genetic engineering.
33) Give four possible problems with genetic engineering.
34) What are the ethical issues concerning 'selective breeding' and 'cloning'?

Section Five — Genetics and Evolution

Population Sizes

Four Factors affect the Individual Organisms

These four physical factors fluctuate throughout the day and year. Organisms <u>live</u>, <u>grow</u> and <u>reproduce</u> in places where, and at times when, these conditions are suitable.

> 1) The <u>temperature</u> — this is rarely ideal for any organism.
>
> 2) The availability of <u>water</u> — vital to all living organisms.
>
> 3) The <u>amount of light available</u> — very important to plants, but it also affects the visibility for animals.
>
> 4) <u>Oxygen</u> and <u>carbon dioxide</u> — these affect respiration and photosynthesis.

The Size of any Population depends on Five Factors

1) The <u>total amount of food</u> or nutrients available.

2) The amount of <u>competition</u> there is (from other species) for the same food or nutrients.

3) The amount of <u>light available</u> (this applies only to plants really).

4) The <u>number</u> of <u>predators</u> (or grazers) who may eat the animal (or plant) in question.

5) <u>Disease</u>.

All these factors help to explain why the <u>types</u> of organisms vary from <u>place to place</u> and from <u>time to time</u>.

The dynamics of plant and animal populations are really quite similar:
<u>Plants</u> often compete with each other for <u>space</u>, and for <u>water</u> and <u>nutrients</u> from the soil.
<u>Animals</u> often compete with each other for <u>space</u>, <u>food</u> and <u>water</u>.

Generally organisms will thrive best if:

1) There's plenty of the <u>good things</u> in life: food, water, space, shelter, light, etc.

2) They're better than the <u>competition</u> at getting it (better *adapted*).

3) They don't get <u>eaten</u>.

4) They don't get <u>ill</u>.

Populations of Prey and Predators go in Cycles

In a community containing prey and predators (as most of them do of course):

1) The <u>population</u> of any species is usually <u>limited</u> by the amount of <u>food</u> available.

2) If the population of the <u>prey</u> increases, then so will the population of the <u>predators</u>.

3) However as the population of predators <u>increases</u>, the number of prey will <u>decrease</u>.

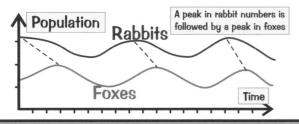

A peak in rabbit numbers is followed by a peak in foxes

i.e. <u>More grass</u> means <u>more rabbits</u>.
More rabbits means <u>more foxes</u>.
But more foxes means <u>less rabbits</u>.
Eventually less rabbits will mean <u>less foxes again</u>.
This <u>up and down pattern</u> continues...

Revision stress — don't let it eat you up...

It's a strange topic is population sizes. In a way it seems like common sense, but it all seems to get so messy. Anyway, <u>learn all the points on this page</u> and you'll be OK with it, I'd think.

Adapt and Survive

If you learn the features that make these animals and plants well adapted, you'll be able to apply them to any other similar creatures they might give you in the Exam.
Chances are you'll get a camel, cactus or polar bear anyway.

The Polar Bear — Designed for Arctic Conditions

The Polar bear has all these features: (which many other Arctic creatures have too, so think on...)

1) Large size and compact shape (i.e. rounded), including dinky little ears, to keep the surface area to a minimum (compared to the body weight) — this all reduces heat loss.

2) A thick layer of blubber for insulation and also to survive hard times when food is scarce.

3) Thick hairy coat for keeping the body heat in.

4) Greasy fur which sheds water after swimming to prevent cooling due to evaporation.

5) White fur to match the surroundings for camouflage.

6) Strong swimmer to catch food in the water and strong runner to run down prey on land.

7) Big feet to spread the weight on snow and ice.

The Camel — Designed for Desert Conditions

The camel has all these features: (most of which are shared by other desert creatures...)

1) It can store a lot of water without problem. It can drink up to 20 gallons at once.

2) It loses very little water. There's little urine and very little sweating.

3) It can tolerate big changes in its own body temperature to remove the need for sweating.

4) Large feet to spread load on soft sand.

5) All fat is stored in the hump, there is no layer of body fat. This helps it to lose body heat.

6) Large surface area. The shape of a camel is anything but compact, which gives it more surface area to lose body heat to its surroundings.

7) Its sandy colour gives good camouflage.

The Cactus is also Well Adapted for the Desert

1) It has no leaves — to reduce water loss.

2) It has a small surface area compared to its size which also reduces water loss. (1000 x less than normal plants)

3) It stores water in its thick stem.

4) Spines stop herbivores eating them.

5) Shallow but very extensive roots ensure water is absorbed quickly over a large area.

Pyramids Of Number and Biomass

This is hideously easy too. Just <u>make sure you know</u> what <u>all</u> the pyramids mean.

Each Trophic Level you go up, there's fewer of them...

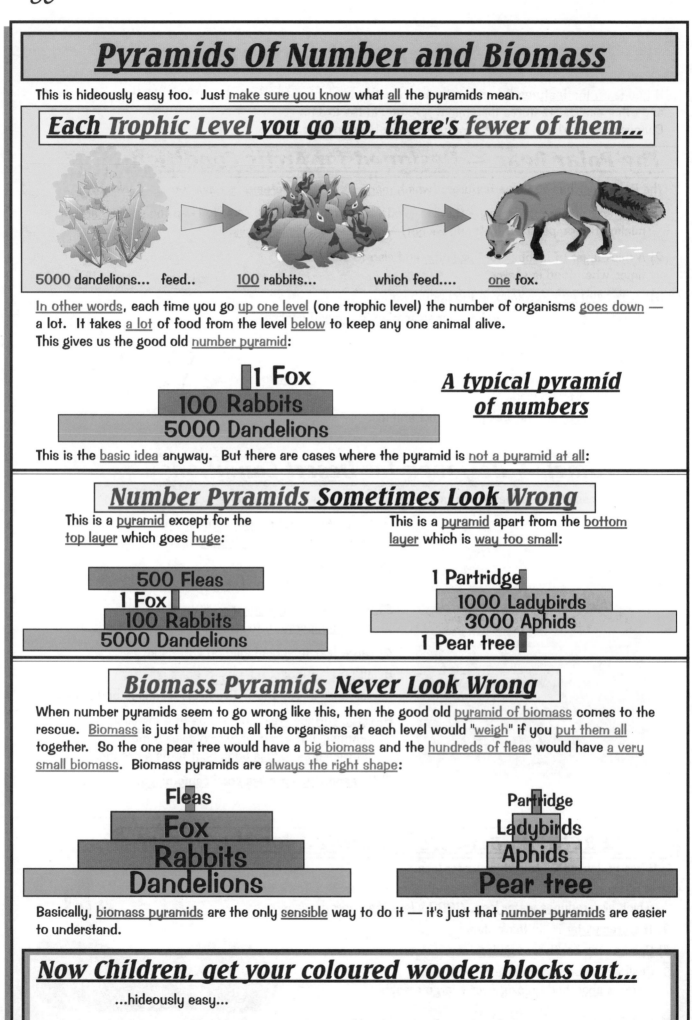

5000 dandelions... feed..   <u>100</u> rabbits...   which feed....   <u>one</u> fox.

<u>In other words</u>, each time you go <u>up one level</u> (one trophic level) the number of organisms <u>goes down</u> — a lot. It takes <u>a lot</u> of food from the level <u>below</u> to keep any one animal alive.
This gives us the good old <u>number pyramid</u>:

1 Fox
100 Rabbits
5000 Dandelions

A typical pyramid of numbers

This is the <u>basic idea</u> anyway. But there are cases where the pyramid is <u>not a pyramid at all</u>:

Number Pyramids Sometimes Look Wrong

This is a <u>pyramid</u> except for the <u>top layer</u> which goes <u>huge</u>:

500 Fleas
1 Fox
100 Rabbits
5000 Dandelions

This is a <u>pyramid</u> apart from the <u>bottom layer</u> which is <u>way too small</u>:

1 Partridge
1000 Ladybirds
3000 Aphids
1 Pear tree

Biomass Pyramids Never Look Wrong

When number pyramids seem to go wrong like this, then the good old <u>pyramid of biomass</u> comes to the rescue. <u>Biomass</u> is just how much all the organisms at each level would "<u>weigh</u>" if you <u>put them all</u> together. So the one pear tree would have a <u>big biomass</u> and the <u>hundreds of fleas</u> would have <u>a very small biomass</u>. Biomass pyramids are <u>always the right shape</u>:

Fleas
Fox
Rabbits
Dandelions

Partridge
Ladybirds
Aphids
Pear tree

Basically, <u>biomass pyramids</u> are the only <u>sensible</u> way to do it — it's just that <u>number pyramids</u> are easier to understand.

Now Children, get your coloured wooden blocks out...

...hideously easy...

Energy Transfer and Efficient Food

All that Energy just Disappears Somehow...

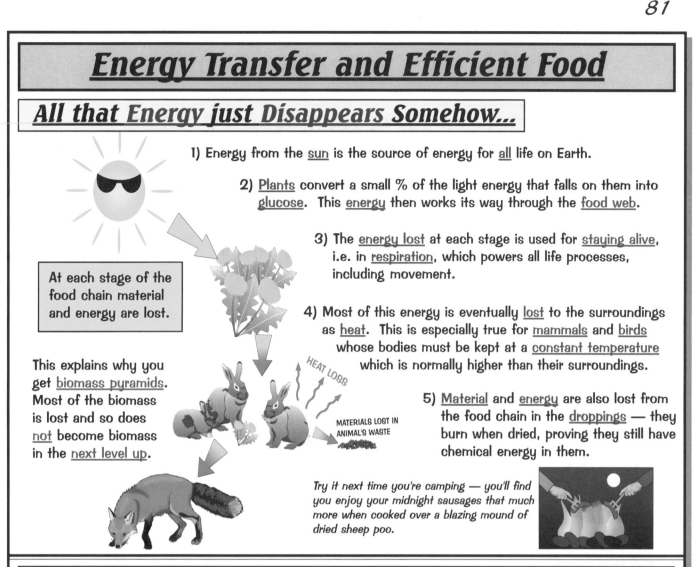

1) Energy from the <u>sun</u> is the source of energy for <u>all</u> life on Earth.

2) <u>Plants</u> convert a small % of the light energy that falls on them into <u>glucose</u>. This <u>energy</u> then works its way through the <u>food web</u>.

3) The <u>energy lost</u> at each stage is used for <u>staying alive</u>, i.e. in <u>respiration</u>, which powers all life processes, including movement.

4) Most of this energy is eventually <u>lost</u> to the surroundings as <u>heat</u>. This is especially true for <u>mammals</u> and <u>birds</u> whose bodies must be kept at a <u>constant temperature</u> which is normally higher than their surroundings.

5) <u>Material</u> and <u>energy</u> are also lost from the food chain in the <u>droppings</u> — they burn when dried, proving they still have chemical energy in them.

At each stage of the food chain material and energy are lost.

This explains why you get <u>biomass pyramids</u>. Most of the biomass is lost and so does <u>not</u> become biomass in the <u>next level up</u>.

HEAT LOSS

MATERIALS LOST IN
ANIMAL'S WASTE

Try it next time you're camping — you'll find you enjoy your midnight sausages that much more when cooked over a blazing mound of dried sheep poo.

Two Ways to Improve the "Efficiency" of Food Production

1) Reducing the Number of Stages in Food Chains

1) For a <u>given area</u> of land, you can produce a lot <u>more food</u> (for humans) by growing <u>crops</u> rather than by <u>grazing animals</u>. This is because you are reducing the number of stages in the food chain. Only <u>10%</u> of what beef cattle eat becomes useful meat for people to eat.

2) However, don't forget that just eating <u>crops</u> can lead to <u>malnutrition</u> through lack of essential <u>proteins</u> and <u>minerals</u>, unless a varied enough diet is achieved. Also remember that some land is <u>unsuitable</u> for growing crops, like <u>moorland</u> or <u>fellsides</u>. In these places, animals like <u>sheep</u> and <u>deer</u> are often the <u>best</u> way to get food from the land.

2) Restricting the Energy Lost by Farm Animals

1) In 'civilised' countries such as ours, animals like <u>pigs</u> and <u>chickens</u> are reared in strict conditions of <u>limited movement</u> and <u>artificial warmth</u>, in order to reduce their <u>energy losses</u> to a minimum.

2) In other words keep them <u>still</u> enough and hot <u>enough</u> and they won't need feeding as much. It's as <u>simple</u> and as <u>horrible</u> as that. If you deny them even the simplest of simple pleasures in their short little stay on this planet before you eat them, then it won't cost you as much in feed. Lovely.

3) But <u>intensively reared</u> animals like chickens and pigs, kept in a little shed all their life, <u>still require land indirectly</u> because they still need <u>feeding</u>, so land is needed to <u>grow</u> their "feed" on. So would it be <u>so terrible</u> to let them have a little corner of it in the sunshine somewhere, huh...?

Locked up in a little cage with no sunlight — who'd work in a bank...

Phew! Just look at all those words crammed onto one page. Geesh.... I mean blimey, it almost looks like a page from a normal science book. Almost. Anyway, there it all is, on the page, just waiting to be blended with the infinite void inside your head. <u>Learn and enjoy</u>... and <u>scribble</u>.

Problems Caused By Farming

Farming Produces a Lot of Food, Which is Great, but...

1) Intensive Farming is important to us because it allows us to produce a lot of food from less and less land.
2) These days it has become quite a high-tech industry. Food production is big business.
3) The great advantage of this is a huge variety of top quality foods, all year round, at cheap prices.
4) This is a far cry from Britain 50 years ago when food had to be rationed by the government because there simply wasn't enough for everyone. That's hard to imagine today... but try...

...Intensive Farming Can Destroy the Environment

Modern methods of farming and agriculture give us the ability to produce plenty of food for everyone. But there's a hefty price to pay. One that we're already paying.

Modern Farming methods can damage the world we live in, making it polluted, unattractive and bereft of wildlife. The main effects are:

1) Removal of hedges to make huge great fields for maximum efficiency. This destroys the natural habitat of many wild creatures, and can lead to serious soil erosion.

2) Loss of meadowlands full of wild flowers, of natural woodlands and orchards of cherry trees, of rolling fields of grass and flowers, and tree-topped hills and leafy lanes — just swept away in a couple of decades.

3) Careless use of fertilisers pollutes rivers and lakes, making them green, slimy and horrible.

4) Pesticides disturb food chains and reduce many insect, bird and mammal populations.

5) Intensive farming of animals such as battery-hens, and crated veal calves is simply indecent.

It *is* possible to farm efficiently and maintain a healthy and beautiful environment. But maximum profit and efficiency will have to be compromised, if we are to make our countryside more than just one big industrial food factory.

Development has to be Sustainable

The Examiners' favourite phrase this year is 'sustainable development'. They've gone potty about it.

> SUSTAINABLE DEVELOPMENT meets the needs of today's population without harming the ability of future generations to meet their own needs.

1) Farming and burning fossil fuels are necessary for our standards of living and there's more demand on them as the population gets bigger.

2) There's only so much abuse our little planet can take. Nowadays, developers can't just build huge power stations or shove stuff in landfills willy-nilly. They have to take greater care to sustain the delicate balance on Earth — the gases in the atmosphere and disposal of waste are just a couple of the things they have to look at.

3) Sustainable development is environmentally friendly. Most development today must be able to continue into the future with as little damage as possible to the planet.

4) In the Exam, make sure you remember the details about the environmental problems development causes. If you get an essay-type question, stick 'em in and show off your 'scientific knowledge'.

5) You'll have to weigh up the pros and cons too.
That's all an essay is — write about the pros, then the cons then make a conclusion.

So much to learn, so little time to learn it...

More environment problems. This stuff can certainly get a bit tedious. At first it can be quite interesting, but then having to make sure you've learnt all those drivelly little details is not.
Still, there's worse things in life than a bit of revision. So learn and enjoy. It's the only way.

Problems Caused By Farming

Pesticides and fertilisers are both artificial chemicals which are spread onto farm land in massive quantities every year. The damaging effects of this haven't always been spotted straight away.

Pesticides Disturb Food Chains

1) Pesticides are sprayed onto most crops to kill the various insects that can damage the crops.
2) Unfortunately, they also kill lots of harmless insects such as bees and beetles.
3) This can cause a shortage of food for many insect-eating birds.
4) Pesticides tend to be poisonous and there's always the danger of the poison passing on to other animals (as well as humans).

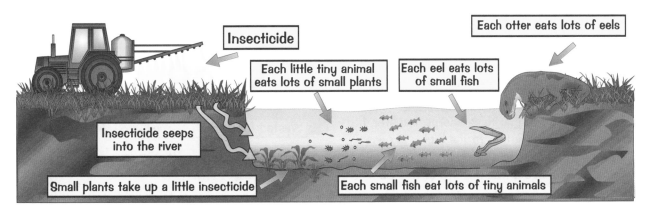

Insecticide

Each otter eats lots of eels

Each little tiny animal eats lots of small plants

Each eel eats lots of small fish

Insecticide seeps into the river

Small plants take up a little insecticide

Each small fish eat lots of tiny animals

This is well illustrated by the case of otters which were almost wiped out over much of crop-dominated Southern England by a pesticide called DDT in the early 1960s. The diagram shows the food chain which ends with the otter. DDT is not excreted so it accumulates along the food chain and the otter ends up with all the DDT collected by all the other animals.

Fertilisers Damage Lakes and Rivers — Eutrophication

1) Fertilisers which contain nitrates are essential to modern farming.
2) Without them crops wouldn't grow nearly so well, and food yields would be well down.
3) This is because the crops take nitrates out of the soil and these nitrates need to be replaced.
4) The problems start if some of the rich fertiliser finds its way into rivers and streams.
5) This happens quite easily if too much fertiliser is applied, especially if it rains soon afterwards.
6) The result is Eutrophication, which basically means "too much of a good thing".
   (Raw sewage pumped into rivers can cause the same problem.)

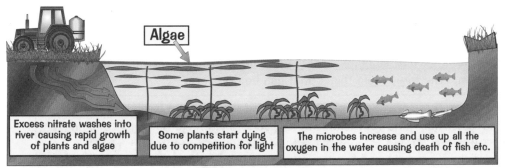

Algae

Excess nitrate washes into river causing rapid growth of plants and algae

Some plants start dying due to competition for light

The microbes increase and use up all the oxygen in the water causing death of fish etc.

As the picture shows, too many nitrates in the water cause a sequence of "mega-growth", "mega-death" and "mega-decay" involving most of the plant and animal life in the water.

7) Farmers need to take a lot more care when spreading artificial fertilisers.

There's nowt wrong wi' just spreadin' muck on it...

Make sure you distinguish between pesticides (which kill bugs and weeds) and fertilisers (which supply nutrients to the plants). They can both cause harm but for totally different reasons. You have to learn the details carefully. Mini-essay time again I'd say. Cover the page and scribble...

Managed Ecosystems

A Salmon Fish Farm Ecosystem in Bonny Scotland

Problem: Fish is becoming an increasingly popular dish, but fish stocks are dwindling.
Solution: "Fish farms" were set up to deliberately rear fish in a controlled way.

Salmon fish farming on the West Coast
of Scotland is the best known example:

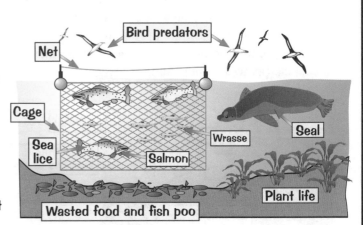

1) The fish are kept in cages in a
   sea-loch, to protect them from predators like
   birds and seals (and other two-legged ones)
   and also to reduce their energy usage due to
   swimming about looking for food — i.e. they
   are kept still to maximise the energy transfer
   from one trophic level to the next.

2) They're fed a carefully controlled diet of food
   pellets, again to maximise energy transfer, but
   also to avoid pollution to the loch. Excess
   food and faeces from the salmon could cause too many bacteria using up the oxygen, so animals
   wouldn't survive at the bottom of the loch.

3) The eggs are artificially fertilised and the young are reared in special tanks to remove any risk from
   predators and ensure as many survive as possible.

4) Fish kept in nets are more prone to disease and parasites. One pest is fish lice and they can be
   treated with a chemical called Dichlorvos which kills them.

5) However, because chemical pesticides tend to linger in the loch and harm other creatures, biological
   pest control is used if possible. One example is the use of a small fish called the wrasse which eats
   fish lice off the backs of the salmon, thus keeping the stock lice-free.

Organic Farming is still perfectly Viable

Modern farming produces a lot of top quality food and we all appreciate it on the supermarket shelves.
However, you certainly could not describe modern farming as "a carefully managed ecosystem" and each
new modern farming technique tends to create various "unforeseen" or "unfore-cared-about"
consequences.

   Traditional farming methods do still work (amazingly!), but they produce rather less food per acre and
it's a bit more expensive too. The positive side to it is that the whole ecosystem stays in balance, the
countryside still looks pretty and the animals get a fair deal too.

   Now that Europe is over-producing food in a big way, it may be time to pay more attention to these
things rather than "maximum food yield at all costs". It is possible to produce plenty of food and still
maintain a balanced ecosystem. The three main things that can be done are:

> 1) Use of organic fertilisers (i.e. spreading muck on it — and there's nowt wrong wi' that).
> 2) Reforestation and "set-aside" land for meadows, to give wild plants and animals a chance.
> 3) Biological control of pests. Trying to control pests which damage crops with other
>   creatures which eat them is a reasonable alternative to using pesticides, and although it's
>   not always quite so effective, at least there are no harmful food chain problems.

Och aye the noo, wee laddie — just learn the fa'acts...

Make sure you can give a good description of a "balanced ecosystem" and a "carefully managed
ecosystem", with examples. Make sure you know why organic farming represents a balanced ecosystem
and why modern farming doesn't. Och aye, an' learn the fa'acts aboot fesh farms...

Conservation

Kill, kill, kill, oops they're all <u>dead</u>. Chop, chop, chop oops they're <u>homeless</u>... and <u>dead</u>.

Conserving Endangered Species and their Habitats

We kill species of plants and animals in <u>two</u> ways:

    1) <u>Directly</u> for food, sport, fur coats, pest control etc.

    2) By destroying their <u>habitats</u>.

If done in a controlled way animal and plant populations will remain at a sustainable level. If done in an <u>uncontrolled</u> way, species will become endangered and (if nothing is done) <u>extinct</u>.

Learn these examples of the problem in Britain:

Example 1: The British Barn Owl is Dying Out

Barn Owls like <u>open</u> areas of <u>rough grassland</u> with hedgerows because this is where <u>voles</u> hang out.
Apart from enjoying the company of voles, Barn Owls like to rip them to bits and swallow them.
Barn Owls live and nest in <u>barns</u> (funny that) and old hollow trees.

Modern farming is destroying the Barn Owl habitat in <u>three</u> ways:

    1) <u>Replacing</u> areas of rough grassland, hedgerows and trees with crop land.

    2) <u>Demolishing</u> old farm buildings, or converting them into houses.

    3) Overuse of <u>pesticides</u> which can poison voles and mice.

    4) Some of the best remaining hunting ground is the rough grassland <u>beside roads</u>. As a result many Barn Owls are <u>killed</u> by passing traffic.

To save the Barn Owl we need to:

1) <u>Replant hedgerows</u>.

2) Allow areas of land to return to an <u>undisturbed habitat</u> to increase mice and vole numbers.

3) Provide <u>nesting boxes</u> in barns, and trees.

(These things are slowly being done as part of <u>sustainable farming</u> projects.)

Example 2: Overfishing North Atlantic Cod

Panda and peas or cod and chips — everyone knows that pandas are rare, but Cod aren't far behind.
Because of the frenzied <u>overfishing</u> this tasty fish could be wiped out from the <u>North Atlantic</u>.

Don't panic yet you crazy cod lovers, there's a <u>four-pronged plan</u>. Learn it well for batter exam results.

1) Fishing <u>quotas</u> to control the numbers of fish killed.

2) Ban on catching <u>juvenile cod</u> to make animal feed.

3) Fishing ban during the <u>three month spawning period</u>.

4) Use of <u>mesh nets</u> that let the juvenile cod escape.

This recovery plan started in <u>June 2001</u>. If it works well, by June 2006
the North sea will produce 10 times more cod than were caught in 2000.

Dodo in batter please...

Conservation questions are going to come up more and more in the exams so put down your cod and chips with barn owl sauce and learn the examples. If they ask you for an example of habitat destruction give 'em the barn owl, if they ask for overfishing give 'em the cod story. Thimple!

There's Too Many People

There's one born every minute — and it's too many

1) The population of the world is currently rising out of control as the graph shows.
2) This is mostly due to modern medicine which has stopped widespread death from disease.
3) It's also due to modern farming methods which can now provide the food needed for so many hungry mouths.
4) The death rate is now much lower than the birth rate in many under-developed countries.
   In other words there are lots more babies born than people dying.

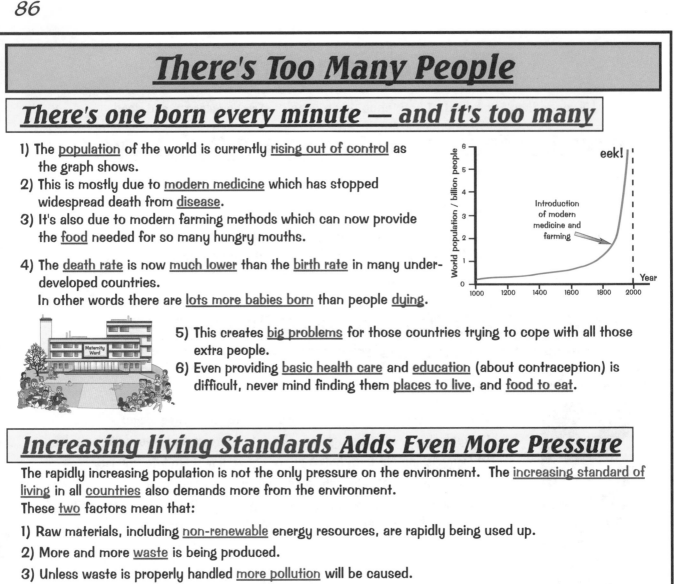

5) This creates big problems for those countries trying to cope with all those extra people.
6) Even providing basic health care and education (about contraception) is difficult, never mind finding them places to live, and food to eat.

Increasing living Standards Adds Even More Pressure

The rapidly increasing population is not the only pressure on the environment. The increasing standard of living in all countries also demands more from the environment.

These two factors mean that:

1) Raw materials, including non-renewable energy resources, are rapidly being used up.

2) More and more waste is being produced.

3) Unless waste is properly handled more pollution will be caused.

When the Earth's population was much smaller, the effects of human activity were usually small and local.

More People Means Less Land for Plants and Animals

There are four main ways that humans reduce the amount of land available for other animals and plants.

1) Building

2) Farming

3) Dumping Waste

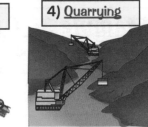
4) Quarrying

More People Means More Environmental Damage

Human activity can pollute all three parts of the environment:
1) Water – with sewage, fertiliser and toxic chemicals.
2) Air – with smoke and gases such as sulphur dioxide.
3) Land – with toxic chemicals, such as pesticides and herbicides.
   These may then be washed from the land into water.

Learn the facts first — then you can build your rocket...

It's real scary innit — the way that graph of world population seems to be pointing nearly vertically upwards... tricky. Anyway, you just worry about your Exams instead, and make sure you learn all the grim facts. Three sections — mini-essays for each, till you know it all.

Section Six — Environment

Atmospheric Pollution

The Three Main Sources of Atmospheric Pollution are...

1) Burning fossil fuels

1) Fossil fuels are coal, oil and natural gas.
2) The main culprits who burn these are cars and power stations.
3) They release mostly carbon dioxide, which is causing the greenhouse effect.
4) But they also release sulphur dioxide and oxides of nitrogen, which are causing acid rain.

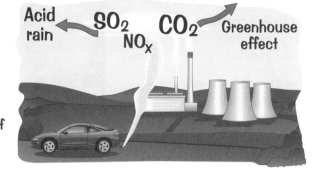

Acid rain ← SO_2 NO_X CO_2 → Greenhouse effect

2) CFC's (Chloro-fluoro-carbons)

1) These are used in aerosols, fridges, air-conditioning units, and polystyrene foam.
2) They are causing a hole in the ozone layer.
3) This allows harmful UV rays to reach the Earth's surface.

3) Lead used in Petrol

1) "Old-fashioned" leaded (4 star) petrol contained lead which pollutes the air.
2) The lead is breathed in and causes damage to the nervous system.

People are usually OK at remembering the three sources of pollution in the atmosphere, but when it comes to sorting out their effects, it's a whole different ball game. You have to make a real effort to learn exactly where each type of pollution comes from and exactly what the effect of each pollutant is. For example, sulphur dioxide does not affect the Greenhouse Effect one squidget, and neither do CFCs. There are dozens of ways to get them all mixed up, but there are no marks for being a clot.

Deforestation increases CO_2 and the Greenhouse Effect

We have already pretty well deforested our country. Now many under-developed tropical countries are doing the same for timber and to provide land for agriculture. If the loss of millions of species wasn't enough this also causes a major increase in the greenhouse gas, carbon dioxide (CO_2). Deforestation increases CO_2 in the atmosphere in two ways:

1) The trees unsuitable for timber are burned releasing CO_2 directly into the atmosphere. Microbes also release CO_2 by decaying the felled trees that remain.

2) Because living trees use CO_2 for photosynthesis, removing these trees means less CO_2 is removed from the atmosphere.

Revision and Pollution — the two bugbears of modern life...

You must make a real effort to sort out the different types of air pollution. Notice for example that cars give out three different things which cause three different problems. Learn it good.

The Greenhouse Effect

Carbon Dioxide and Methane Trap Heat *from the Sun*

1) The <u>temperature</u> of the Earth is a <u>balance</u> between the heat it gets from the sun and the heat it radiates back out into space.

2) The <u>atmosphere</u> acts like an <u>insulating layer</u> and keeps some of the heat <u>in</u>.

3) This is exactly what happens in a <u>greenhouse</u> or a <u>conservatory</u>.

   The sun shines <u>into it</u> and the glass keeps the <u>heat in</u> so it just gets <u>hotter</u> and <u>hotter</u>.

Light energy from the Sun

Layer of CO_2 and Methane

Heat radiation reflected back to Earth

4) There are several different gases in the atmosphere which are very good at keeping the <u>heat in</u>. They are called "<u>greenhouse gases</u>", oddly enough. The <u>main ones</u> that we worry about are <u>methane</u> and <u>carbon dioxide</u>, because the levels of these are rising quite sharply.

5) Human activity is increasing the <u>Greenhouse Effect</u> causing the Earth to <u>warm up</u> very slowly.

The Greenhouse Effect *may cause* Flooding *and* Drought ....(!)

1) Changes in weather patterns and climate could cause problems of <u>drought</u> or <u>flooding</u>.

2) The <u>melting</u> of the polar ice-caps would <u>raise sea-levels</u> and could cause <u>flooding</u> to many <u>low-lying coastal parts</u> of the world including many <u>major cities</u>.

Modern Industrial Life *is Increasing the* Greenhouse Effect

1) The level of <u>CO_2</u> in the atmosphere used to be nicely <u>balanced</u> between the CO_2 released by <u>respiration</u> (of animals and plants) and the CO_2 absorbed by <u>photosynthesis</u>.

2) However, mankind has been burning <u>massive amounts</u> of <u>fossil fuels</u> in the last two hundred years or so.

3) We have also been <u>cutting down trees</u> all over the world to make space for living and farming. This is called <u>deforestation</u>.

4) The level of CO_2 in the atmosphere has <u>gone up</u> by about <u>20%</u>, and will <u>continue to rise</u> ever more steeply as long as we keep <u>burning fossil fuels</u> — just look at that graph — eek!

% CO_2 in atmosphere

0.036 0.035 0.034 0.033 0.032 0.031 0.030 0.029 0.028 0.027

Year

1700 1750 1800 1850 1900 1950 2000

Temp (°C)

0.5 0.25 average -0.25 -0.5

Year

1850 1900 1950 2000

Methane *is Also a Problem*

1) <u>Methane gas</u> is also contributing to the <u>Greenhouse Effect</u>.

2) It's produced <u>naturally</u> from various sources, such as <u>natural marshland</u>.

3) However, the two sources of methane which are <u>on the increase</u> are:

   a) <u>Rice growing</u>

   b) <u>Cattle rearing</u> — it's the cows "pumping" that's the problem, believe it or not.

Learn the facts first — then start building your ark...

I bet you never realised there were so many drivelly details on the Greenhouse Effect. Well there <u>are</u> and I'm afraid they could all come up in your Exam, so you just gotta learn them. Use the good old <u>mini-essay</u> method for each section, and <u>scribble down what you know</u>...

Acid Rain

Burning Fossil Fuels Causes Acid Rain

1) When fossil fuels are burned they release mostly carbon dioxide which is increasing the Greenhouse Effect. They also release two other harmful gases:

   a) sulphur dioxide   b) various nitrogen oxides.

2) When these mix with clouds they form acids. This then falls as acid rain.

3) Cars and power stations are the main causes of acid rain.

Acid Rain Kills Fish, Trees and Statues

1) Acid rain causes lakes to become acidic which has a severe effect on its ecosystem.

2) The way this happens is that the acid causes aluminium salts (in the soil) to dissolve into the water. The resulting aluminium ions are poisonous to many fish and birds.

3) Acid rain kills trees.

4) Acid rain damages limestone buildings and ruins stone statues.

Acid Rain is Prevented by Cleaning up Emissions

1) Power stations now have Acid Gas Scrubbers to take the harmful gases out before they release their fumes into the atmosphere.

2) Cars are now being fitted with catalytic converters to clean up their exhaust gases.

3) The other way of reducing acid rain is simply to reduce our usage of fossil fuels.

Catalytic converter

Learn about Acid Rain — and always take a coat...

There aren't too many details on acid rain. If you can't learn all this lot properly then you're just not trying. Don't forget they won't ask you easy stuff like "Is acid rain caused by cars or monkeys?", they'll test you on trickier stuff like "Which gases cause acid rain and why?". Learn and enjoy. And smile.

Decomposition and The Carbon Cycle

Another sixties pop group? Sadly not.

1) Living things are made of materials they take from the world around them.
2) When they decompose, ashes are returned to ashes, and dust to dust, as it were.
3) In other words the elements they contain are returned to the soil where they came from originally.
4) These elements are then used by plants to grow and the whole cycle repeats over and over again.

Decomposition is carried out by Bacteria and Fungi

1) All plant matter and dead animals are broken down and decomposed by soil bacteria and fungi.
2) This happens everywhere in nature, and also in compost heaps and sewage works.
3) All the important elements are thus recycled:
   Carbon, Hydrogen, Oxygen and Nitrogen.
4) The ideal conditions for creating compost are:
   a) Warmth
   b) Moisture
   c) Oxygen (air)
   d) Decomposers (i.e. bacteria and fungi)
   e) Organic matter cut into small pieces.
      Make sure you learn them — all five.

Extra decomposers added (compost maker)

Finely shredded waste is best

Warmth generated by decomposition helps it all along

Mesh sides to let air in

There's a kid I know, and everyone calls him "the party mushroom". I'm not sure why really — they just say he's a fun guy to be with...

The Carbon Cycle Shows how Carbon is Recycled

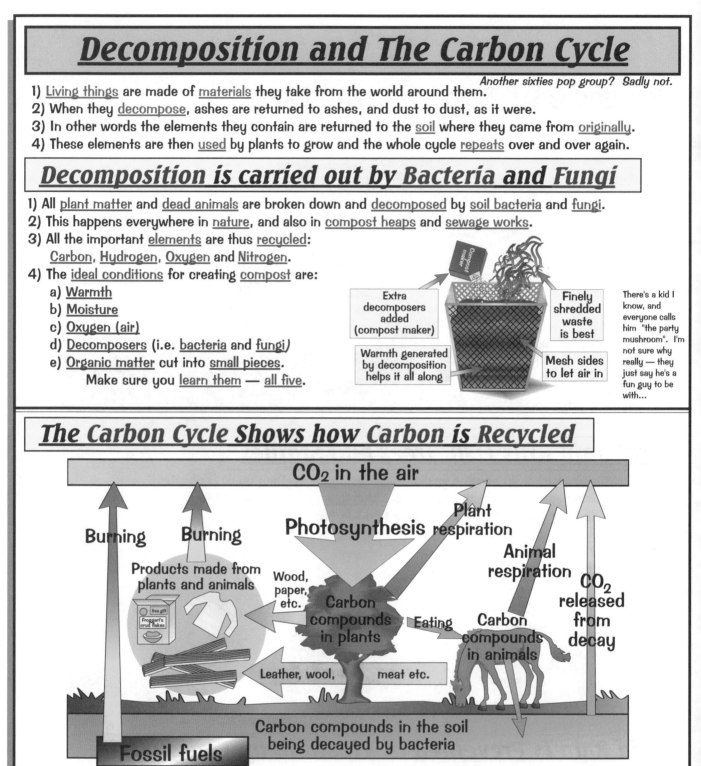

CO_2 in the air

Burning   Burning   Photosynthesis   Plant respiration   Animal respiration CO_2 released from decay

Products made from plants and animals

Wood, paper, etc.

Carbon compounds in plants

Eating

Carbon compounds in animals

Froggart's crud flakes   free gift

Leather, wool,   meat etc.

Fossil fuels

Carbon compounds in the soil being decayed by bacteria

This diagram isn't half as bad as it looks. Learn these important points:
1) There's only one arrow going down. The whole thing is "powered" by photosynthesis.
2) Both plant and animal respiration puts CO_2 back into the atmosphere.
3) Plants convert the carbon in CO_2 from the air into fats, carbohydrates and proteins.
4) These can then go three ways: be eaten, decay or be turned into useful products by people.
5) Eating transfers some of the fats, proteins and carbohydrates to new fats, carbohydrates and proteins in the animal doing the eating.
6) Ultimately these plant and animal products either decay or are burned and CO_2 is released.

On Ilkley Moor ba 'tat, On Ilkley Moor ba 'tat... *...where the dogs play football...*

Learn the five ideal conditions for compost making. They like asking about that.
There's another version of the carbon cycle in the Chemistry Book which you really should look at, but this one is easier to understand. Practise scribbling it out from memory. And keep trying till you can.

The Nitrogen Cycle

The <u>constant cycling</u> of nitrogen through the atmosphere, soil and living organisms is called the <u>nitrogen cycle</u>.

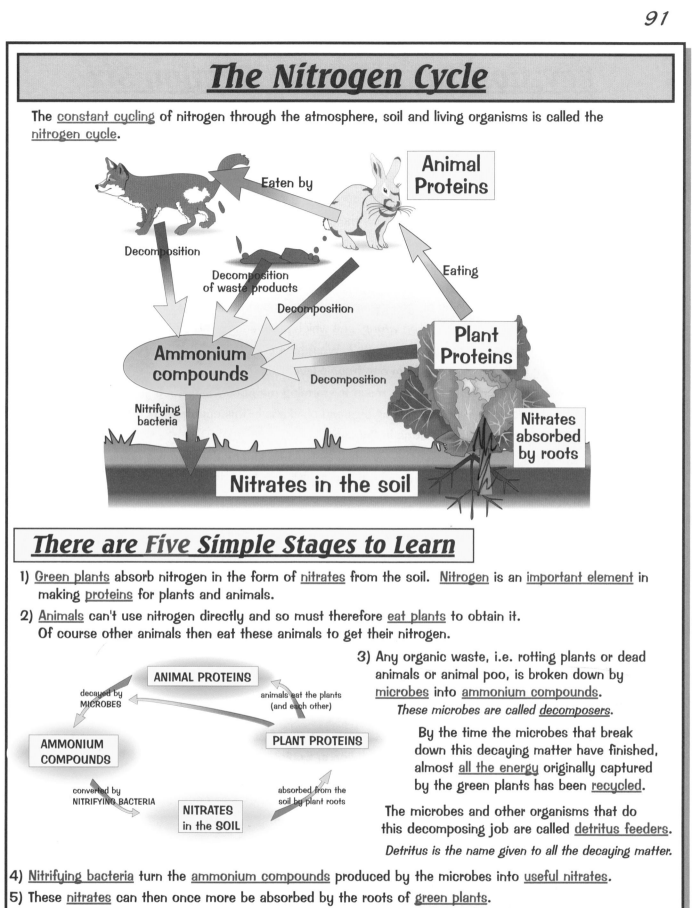

There are Five Simple Stages to Learn

1) <u>Green plants</u> absorb nitrogen in the form of <u>nitrates</u> from the soil. <u>Nitrogen</u> is an <u>important element</u> in making <u>proteins</u> for plants and animals.

2) <u>Animals</u> can't use nitrogen directly and so must therefore <u>eat plants</u> to obtain it.
Of course other animals then eat these animals to get their nitrogen.

3) Any organic waste, i.e. rotting plants or dead animals or animal poo, is broken down by <u>microbes</u> into <u>ammonium compounds</u>.
These microbes are called <u>decomposers</u>.

By the time the microbes that break down this decaying matter have finished, almost <u>all the energy</u> originally captured by the green plants has been <u>recycled</u>.

The microbes and other organisms that do this decomposing job are called <u>detritus feeders</u>.

Detritus is the name given to all the decaying matter.

4) <u>Nitrifying bacteria</u> turn the <u>ammonium compounds</u> produced by the microbes into <u>useful nitrates</u>.

5) These <u>nitrates</u> can then once more be absorbed by the roots of <u>green plants</u>.

One more thing you should know — some nitrates used by plants are in the soil because of <u>nitrogen fixing bacteria</u>. These bacteria turn <u>nitrogen gas</u> from the air into nitrates in the soil. Other bacteria, called <u>denitrifying bacteria</u>, do the opposite. They turn nitrates in the soil back into nitrogen gas.

By Gum, you young 'uns have some stuff to learn...

It's really "grisly grimsdike" is the Nitrogen Cycle, I think. But the fun guys at the Exam Boards want you to know all about it, so there you go. <u>Have a good time</u>... *and smile!*

Revision Summary for Section Six

There's a lot of words in Section Six. Most topics are pretty waffly with a lot of drivelly facts, and it can be real hard to learn them all. But learn them you must. You need to practise scribbling down what you can remember on each topic, and then checking back to see what you missed. These questions give you a pretty good idea of what you should know. You need to practise and practise them — till you can float through them all, like a cloud or something.

1) What are the *four* basic things which determine the size of a population of a species?

2) Sketch a graph of prey and predator populations and explain the shapes.

3) List seven survival features of the polar bear and of the camel.

4) Give five survival features for the cactus.

5) What are number pyramids? Why do you generally get a pyramid of numbers?

6) Why do number pyramids sometimes go wrong, and which pyramids are always right?

7) Where does the energy in a food chain originate? What happens to the energy?

8) How much energy and biomass pass from one trophic level to the next?

9) Where does the rest go? What does this mean for farming methods where food is scarce?

10) How is this idea used to cut costs in rearing pigs and chickens in this country? Is it nice?

11) Describe the details of salmon fish farms in Scotland.

12) Explain why organic farming represents a balanced ecosystem and modern farming doesn't.

13) Give four reasons why Barn Owls are dying out and explain what needs to be done to save them.

14) What's being done to save North Atlantic Cod?

15) Why are chemical pesticides used? What are the drawbacks of doing this?

16) Explain in detail how pesticides enter the food chain. What happened with DDT in the '60s?

17) What happens when too much nitrate fertiliser is put onto fields? Give full details.

18) What is the big fancy name given to this problem? How can it be avoided?

19) What is happening to the world population? What is largely responsible for this trend?

20) What can be said about the birth rate and death rate in developing countries?

21) What problems does a rapidly increasing population create for a country?

22) What effect does more and more people have on the environment?

23) What are the three main sources of atmospheric pollution?

24) What are the precise environmental effects of each of these three sources of pollution?

25) What does CFC stand for? Where do CFCs come from? What damage do they do?

26) List the four problems resulting from deforestation in tropical countries. Why do they do it?

27) Which two gases are increasing of the Greenhouse Effect?

28) Explain how the greenhouse effect happens. What dire consequences could there be?

29) What is causing the rise in levels of each of the two problem gases. What is the solution?

30) Which gases cause acid rain? Where do these gases come from?

31) What are the three main harmful effects of acid rain? Explain exactly how fish are killed.

32) Give three ways that acid rain can be reduced.

33) Which two organisms are responsible for the decay of organic matter?

34) What are the five ideal conditions for making compost? Draw a compost maker.

35) What is the Carbon Cycle all to do with? Draw as much of it from memory as you can.

36) What is the Nitrogen Cycle all about? Draw as much of it from memory as you can.

Index

Index

Index

Index